THE HUE-MA

A Genetic Odyssey

By Pi Rah Hotep

TABLE OF CONTENTS

EGO = 1 / KNOWLEDGE

It's important to keep your ego balanced, Mathematics is the soul of our existence.

Albert Einstein

"Knowledge is the only meaningful resource today". *- Peter Drucker (1999)*

"Being unconscious, unfocused, unorganised, and detached from our purpose has become the daily normal state of mind for our people".

*A revamped version by ASA G. HILLIARD, III Ed. D

To secure results it's important to understand the law and comply with it. Those of you who realise that power comes from within and that we are weak only because we are dependent on help from and who hesitantly throws himself on his thoughts instantly rights himself, stands firm, assumes a dominant attitude, and works miracles.

African Creation Energy

If you can't learn the art of saying a few words meaning a lot rather than saying a lot and meaning very little It is better to be silent or say very little.

Abraham Lincoln - Revamped

THE GOD CODE

$Gij,j=0$

Gabriel Audu Oyibo is a Nigerian mathematician who solved the Grand Unification Theory - popularly known as the "Theory of Everything" or "The Holy Grail of Mathematics and Physics", in 1990, by discovering the GOD Almighty's Grand Unified Theorem (GAGUT) which is represented by an exact mathematical equation $Gij,j=0$, that can be interpreted as GOD (Gij), in GOD's Material (i) and Space-Time (j) Dimensions, does not change, where the comma symbolizes the change in tensor notation. Gij could also represent everything in the Universe including the Unified Force Field, all of its components, all particles, both atomic as well as subatomic including all quarks, and leptons and all of their interactions. In a simple language, GAGUT states that GOD or everything including the Unified Force Field or any fundamental force or particle interactions, is conserved within a transformation process over space and time, which cannot be disputed by ANY logical process. It is therefore the provable truth or theorem of everything which has no possibility of errors logically or geometrically.

GAGUT also proved geometrically that Hydrogen, also called Africanium, is the only real element on the periodic table of "elements" while the remaining 117 previously called "elements" are nuclear compounds of Hydrogen or Africanium, which now has the potential of making science 118 times simpler to study.

NOTHING IS WRONG WITH US

SOMETHING HAPPENED TO US

Rev. Dr. Philippe SHOCK Matthews

Undated handout illustration

The universe and everything in it is The Creator; the universe does not expand. O Africanium (formerly known as hydrogen) is the only real element. All others are compounds of Africanium. O Black people are closest to the Creator. Black, as we know, is the first energy frequency of the First One.

Africa is the origin of all things and also the origin of civilization which they have buried and they hide under their museums. You are the origin, not Sumeria, not Babylon, you are. And one of those great civilizations was Kemet, which was overthrown by several different groups. They have been on the hunt for the pharaonic bloodlines to revive it and they have broken the code of the pharaohs. This leader that will come, they will claim that this leader will be of the bloodline of the Pharaohs, which it will not be. 'Do not trust or believe this leader'. The reason why they are after Africa, Africa is the origin of mathematics, you are the origin of astrology, you are the origin of writing, it is not Europe, it is not Sumeria, it is not Babylon, it is you, Africa.

The lebombo bone, the Ishango bone, was a calculator, you have Adam's Calendar. One hundred and fifty thousand years ago, smelting gold, iron, steel, copper in southern Africa. The origin of metallurgy is you. Then we get to genetics, the origin of where the human race of every colour comes from is you and with you it will end. But you don't understand what you are fighting!!

Empress, Rainetta Jones 2015

A LESSON LEARNT

We are all here to learn certain lessons. Those lessons are found in our personal code. Every number contains a divine attribute of the Creator, talents, and qualities that are given at birth. These qualities react according to its vibrational content and tunes into the vibration of your code in order to fulfill it (vibration)

Black is a unique colour (some argue that it's not even a colour) in that it is surprisingly multifaceted. It conveys so many things - moodiness, mystery, elegance, sophistication, class and even death. It's deceptive in that it appears limiting but in reality is that it can do so many things. The most dramatic of all colours, it offers something that no other colour can: a finality or poise. As the German physicist, *Hermann Von Helmhoz*, declared: 'Black is a real sensation, even if it is produced by the entire absence of light. The sensation of black is distinctly different from the lack of all sensation'.

Scientists have discovered secret code hiding within DNA which instructs cells on how genes are controlled. Scripture declares how the creator writes His instructions - teachings in the heart (soul, inner man, Jer.31 :31-34). The amazing discovery is expected to open new doors to the diagnosis and treatment of diseases according to new studies. Ever since the genetic code was deciphered over 40 years ago, scientists have believed that it only described how proteins are made. However, the revelation made by a research team led by John Stamatoyannopoulos of the University of Washington indicates that genomes use the genetic code to write two separate languages.

Scientists discovered that the second language instructs the cells on how genes are controlled, according to findings published in 'Science Magazine'. The second language remained hidden for so long because one language was written on top of the other, scientists said. One of the codes uses a 64-letter alphabet called codons. The researchers also discovered that many of these codons have two meanings - one related to proteins (health), and the other related gene control (movement).

DISCUSSION QUESTIONS

- How many elements are there on the periodic table?
- What is the difference between a formula and an expression?

QUEST FOR KNOWLEDGE SEARCH FOR TRUTH
What you are about to read constitutes the most extensive
research project I have ever conducted. No theory of
mathematics that deals only with mathematics will ever explain
mathematics. I believe that as we go on trying to understand the
universe, we are at the same time trying to understand ourselves
as hue-mans.

Your mind is part of a universal mind, for it to flower it has to
go beyond what it knows. You are the ancestor of the future,
your heartbeat should align with that of the universe and nature's
natural forces. You are the mysterious potential of the
future. This is the time to remember how to align ourselves and
live with the natural forces

The hue-man Code (x) is dedicated to the thinker - which I
assume you are, otherwise, you would probably not be reading
what was in my mind. We are all fundamental participants in
the process of creation.

I have come to recognise that hue-man life, its origins, and its
future were predicated upon forces dictated by the natural
world. Paleontology, planetary mathematics, astrophysics, and

the other natural sciences were shaping who we are, how we came about, and what lies in store for us. Our origins certainly were not the by-product of some omnipotent, godfather deity who created the universe in six days and rested on the seventh. Many of the wondrous events associated with the Son in the gospel became difficult to accept as amazing historical events. At the start of the twentieth century, an informant from the pawnee tribe of the American plains once told an ethnographer, "All that the stars did in the heavens foretold what would befall upon the earth", for as yet the earth was not made. That comment highlights Pawnee astrologers perception of the celestial sky - as a pictographic script depicting primordial events.

Long before the invention of GPS or compasses, people had already started their journey. How? Instead of looking into the screen, they look up into the night sky seeking for answers from these eternal light beads. In fact, before anyone understood what stars are, people had already formed their own belief about them. In North America, aboriginal tribes have different views on the meaning of stars. Some believe that the night sky has spiritual significance, and some believe that twinkling objects have similar human characteristics. Astronomy played an important role in the early native American culture; it was even the basis of governance and agricultural practice. The study of stars has also led tribes to theorize about the origin of life in the universe.

This practice is evident among the Navajo of modern Arizona as well; Navajo even stress the reason that scriptures were "written" in the stars. In her exploration of Navajo celestial mythology, anthropologist *Trudy Griffin-Pierce (1992)* reports: When all the stars were ready to be placed in the sky, First Woman [who is both hue-man and deity] said, "I will use these to write the laws that are to govern mankind for all time. These laws cannot be written on water as that is always changing its form, nor can they be written in the sand as the wind would soon erase them, but if they are written in the stars they can be read and remembered forever".

Irrespective of your point of view, the universe is subject to hierarchic orders simply because nothing could ever interact with anything if it were not for the orderly and logical mechanisms governed by coded law. Hue-man society represents one of the most eloquent examples of this truth. The majority of us hue-mans in existing societies are not aware of our true identities, which explains, in some part, the contagious trend of hero worship and the multiplicity of religions and societies.

Numbers, sequences, symbols and codes are all part of nature, you cannot put up a fight against anything natural. Once you become consciously aware of this it implies that you have successfully climbed the higher ranks of *code* hierarchy

The Hue-man Code, offers you a highly effective and exciting journey in discovering and exploring the truth of your real identity. The book explores who you are and how to access your *code*. If you can put these teachings into practice, you will discover your true self and your place as a living god and more than an equal amongst others.

DISCUSSION QUESTION
- Which woman contributed to the invention of the GPS?
- Name the co-author of the 1985 classic, The Heart Of the Race?

FOREWORD

By Rev. Dr. Philippe SHOCK Matthews

The Hue-man Code: A Genetic Odyssey

What if you discovered you were born with a cosmic signature that if properly decoded could permanently and positively alter the course of your life? Well, that is the power of knowing your Hue-man Code by PI Ratio.

As one of the world's leading mathematicians, PI Ratio's Hue-man Code discovery is equal to if not surpassing the discovery of the God code known as GAGUT (God Almighty Grand Unified Theorem) by Dr. Gabriel Oyibo. The Hue-man code applies a special mathematical calculation to your Earthday, Bornday, or what most know as your birthday.

Within your birthday is a special, hidden sequence or signal of code and mathematical equations that gives you a blueprint or homing signal that allows you to always find your true north no matter how lost in the world you may have become. Ironically, math was created by Amma's (The Creator's) firstborn, the African woman who began counting her moon cycles, making the Black woman the original mother goddess. From that point on, nature became our greatest teacher as the first Africans literally developed a frequency, a 1st Frequency that could never be destroyed.

As I have developed a hierarchical, theosophical framework based on social science called the 4 Metaphysical Frequencies, PI Ratio's hue-man code is the spiritual technology and mathematical map that all 1st Frequency Africans/African Americans may use to assist us in the restoration of our original signal created by Amma (The Creator) when we emerged out of the waters of Nun (womb) and took our first breath. The hue-man code is like a beacon device; helping Black people overcome the continuous signal interruption from 2nd frequency people who are responsible for producing the lower frequencies of 3rd and 4th, aka the negro and the nigga respectfully.

1ST FREQUENCY

1st Frequency is your original signal as it represents the first idea of Amma (The Creator). When Amma decided to imitate, duplicate, and replicate itself in hue-man form the first African was born; hence, 1st Frequency. Because the African is Amma made (As Above), there is nothing on this Earth we cannot conquer and endure (As Below). When we say to ourselves we are made in the image and likeness of our Creator, that Creator is the carbon, quantum field which is the essence of all colors and manifests as highly melanated offspring. Before light can be seen, darkness (matter) must always first be present.

2ND FREQUENCY

The 2nd frequency represents the human mutation of a mutation, referred to today as the European or Eurasian. During the African migration and populating the Earth, a group of Africans got trapped in the Wurm glaciation or ice age for more than one hundred thousand years, the African trapped in the ice did not evolve it devolved (mutated) into an anti-African (anti-Christ), callous creature, initiating the process and instruction from nature to depigment itself (lack of melanin), which created a recessively genetic human desperately wanting to be a "being" but lost its ability to connect to its 1st Frequency (carbon) signal and move back into Black or the original hue-man family, permanently making the 2nd frequency European a mutation of a mutation.

Theologian, Dr. AJ Vrarmah in a lecture on 1st Frequency of Oneness/Shock Metaphysics, referred to 2nd frequency people as "hueless humanoids" in the two-part episode of "Why Genetics Is A Touchy Subject" and according to Rev. Billy Bman Byrd, author of The Black Room: Protect Your Black Mind Body Spirit And Soul, referred to 2nd frequency as a "Widespread worldwide occurrence of an infectious disease rooted in the destruction of the Melanated community," creating what he refers to as "Second Frequency-White-ism-White-ness is a viral Coronavirus (COVID-19) like sickness and an enemy of the hue-man family."

3RD FREQUENCY

In order for this recessively genetic, 2nd frequency species to survive in an all-hue-man, melanated world they had to create a domination process known as colonialism (white supremacy), and specifically in the United States when they invented a false racial construct as a matter of colonial law called "white" people between 1664 and 1681. This was the birth of what Dr. Francis Cress Welsing and Dr. Neely Fuller refer to as "white supremacy." When white people were invented, the 2nd frequency, recessive genetic mutation renamed the 1st Frequency, aboriginal African on US soil and those they stole and enslaved from the Continent (Africa) to Nigger/Negro (3rd frequency).

The nigger/negro is a 3rd frequency signal of survival, assimilation, domestication, and colonization that for the last five hundred years created a generational (epigenetic) amnesia and illusion in the original 1st Frequency African/African American (aka Black People) that Dr. Oba T'Shaka refers to in the Six-Fold Stages to Mental Freedom as Black Identity.

4TH FREQUENCY

Due to the constant oppressive, suppressive, and depressive signal omitted from 2nd frequency people, the African/African American has been generationally traumatized and socially engineered via a constant state of RBF (Racial Battle Fatigue), the fuel for systemic, institutionalized, scientific racism that has caused Black people, particularly the African Americans to produce a rebellious, psychotic, mentally ill state of self-oppression and self-hate we now call the Nigga (4th frequency).

4th Frequency is the frequency of self-deprivation, learned hopelessness/helplessness whereas the 1st Frequency, Amma amnesiacs refers to themselves as bitches, ho's, thugs, thots, baby mamas, baby daddies, ratchet, and of course, real niggas. When the self-concept of the African/African American is hijacked, you lose a sense of self and your esteem becomes vacant as outlined by Dr. Joy DeGruy's in her seminal work: PTSS (Post Traumatic Slave Syndrome).

Because the African/African American has never been introduced to a higherarcial, theosophical social science that gives them a blueprint to their original, 1st Frequency signal (who they really are), Black people worldwide have been catapulted into a perpetual state of psychotic racial despair that has caused us to become complicit in our own self-destruction and self-annihilation (genocide, suicide, homicide). Hence, the captured, corralled and controlled Black person suffers from capture bonding (Stockholm Syndrome) and trauma bonding no differently than a POW (Prisoner of War).

When we are incarnated, before the signal interruption of 2nd frequency aamu, the 1st Frequency Africans had ample time to evolve into their natural 1st Frequency nature. We were unfettered and unbound until the conflicted consciousness of 2nd frequency slowly began stifling, hampering, blocking, and interrupting our original hue-man code and we (Africans) began a rapid descent into madness that today we attempt to make sense of through 3rd frequency and 4th frequency: negros/niggas identities.

I urge all 1st Frequency Africans/African Americans to devour the knowledge and wisdom of this masterpiece book then contact PI Ratio for your personal hue-man, bar code reading. When you discover your Hue-Man Code, you must then go into your Black Room to activate it which will begin waking you up to your 1st Frequency signal where you learn how to become a walking living Amma (God/Goddess) as you were meant to be before your original signal was rudely interrupted.

Repeat 7 times per day for 7 days:

I am One with 1st Frequency
I am One with the First Thought Idea
I am One with the First Born People
I am One with the Only One!

Ase

And So It Is

Rev. Dr. Philippe SHOCK Matthews

Founder: 1st Frequency of Oneness, Science, Manifestation and Prosperity (www.1stFrequency.com)

PREFACE

How many of us are hooked on self-help theorems? For me, it started about 7 years ago. I felt it was time to take myself to another level. Tired of this hand-to-mouth syndrome that seemed to follow me wherever I went, whatever I did I couldn't shake this damn monkey off my back. Have you ever been in a situation where you work as hard as you can, do the best you think you can and it is never enough. At the end of the month, you are still trying to make the pennies or the pounds add up. I had had enough of feeling useless, having to make my children feel that buying certain things at the supermarket was a luxury when it should be a standard choice.

I have brought numerous books on self-help from many big-hitting authors who I won't name. I was hooked on changing my life and the life of my family. Finally, I was going to get rid of this 'hand-to-mouth' syndrome. Self-development consumed me... I started paying attention to the food I was eating, I started working out, my passion for mathematics I started taking it more seriously. I started reading book after book after book. There were too many so-called gurus to follow but I tried to keep up as best as I could. Getting up early, working out, taking cold showers, reading affirmations to myself, visualizing my goals. I felt more confident than ever before, this is it I said to myself, everything was beginning to fit in place, at least that is what I wanted other people to think.

I realized that there were some glaring issues that I had to face up to. Yes, I wanted to change my life, my current situation. I had seriously had enough of having enough, I wanted more happiness, money, I wanted to prove to those who doubted my ability who don't believe I can achieve anything great.

It took me a very long time to start investing in these self-help notions as I always believed that I didn't need the help that they said they were offering. The biggest reason we seek this help is that we have a big dissatisfaction with ourselves or where we are currently at... Wanting to change your current situation or where you are at is a powerful thing to do. The problem with this is your vulnerability, especially if you are in a dark place and you are looking to escape from it. Many of these notions have an amazing lure to them, a world of people trying to create better versions of themselves. A world that makes you feel you are taking control of your life and your decisions, an environment full of progress.

Reading a self-help book from start to finish has an amazing feeling of satisfaction, you feel a sense of purpose. A surge of dopamine rises straight to your head after every task/book is completed. I would then be ready to jump online and order another book, not realising that I was now on this vicious cycle (a bit like the hamster on a wheel), not seeing any end... Once you take time out to pause and reflect, what has changed? nothing!! In the book Unscripted by *M.J. Demarco,* there is a concept called "Áction Faking" Doing things that make you think you're making progress when you're not. It's a bit like creating a schedule and calling it a day's work or buying business cards instead of picking up the phone and making a sale. This is a lethal form of procrastination.

Many of us consume too much with very little action. The consequences can often be dramatic: an empty wallet, a whole bunch of temporary motivation, and a gut-wrenching feeling of realisation that you have achieved nothing and made no progress. The only thing that has changed is that you have got better at convincing yourself you did.

DISCUSSION QUESTIONS

- When was the last time you had had enough of having enough?
- Have you ever subscribed to a self-help program that changed your fortune? If so, how?

CONVENTION USED

Introducing this relatively new and specialized way of code access, I have endeavoured to make the content accessible to readers with little or no knowledge of 'The hue-man code and personal access. What has been written reflects the wisdom of many ancestral generations from the African continent. This book has no theory to prove no agenda to push, and no one to impress. Accessing your code will not resolve a broken marriage or relationship, or even correct behavioural problems. But what will transpire is the possibility of rah-membering that all matters of the heart are initiated by your code, and it is to this source that our attention needs to focus on when considering the wellbeing and health, not only of ourselves but also our relationships and families.

The view of us as hue-man, in many ways, is vastly different from the one that is familiar to the *'wazungu'*. We have learnt from our ancestors that family life and relationships are a gift, similar to our code which requires gratitude and a willingness as hue-mans to work together as it is essential to our existence as a people. If we can understand that our code is for the fulfilment of one's life purpose, allowing you to offer the gift you carry around within.

Much of what will be shared in this book cannot be grasped like data or inserted into some form of statistics. Others will find certain aspects difficult for their logical mind to grab hold of and thereby defies being another commodity for consumption.

Our code offers us a mature vision and challenges every one of us to become more of who we are and less of what others want us to be...

It's important to also note that our current understanding of our code is primarily a coded order ordained and authorised by the creator, and executed by someone who recognises that he/she cannot, by themselves, make happen what they have been invited to. Our code reminds us how close to earth and nature we are. To this end, terms are specific to 1st, 3rd & 4th frequency.

DISCUSSION QUESTIONS

- Do you have a problem being referred to as 'black'? If so, why?
- What is an equation?

INTRO

This book is full of thought and talk, but the result of thought and talk should be the ability to make choices.

Today - right at this moment - in every part of the world, some wonder what they can do to get further along toward some shining goal and to their self-improvement.

Many will snatch a secret from the depths of their heart and souls that will drive them on to high achievement. But the majority will continue to wonder … dream … and wish.

Everyone Wants Something - No matter what it is: money, position, prestige ... some special achievement ... the opportunity to be of service to his fellowmen ... love, a happy marriage and a happy home. Everyone yearns for some kind of fulfilment-success in some form. To be happy, to be healthy, wealthy, and to experience the true riches of life-these are universal desires. It's these inner desires and urges that inspire and motivate us into action. You and I are no exception and you have the same opportunity as others.

Bryon in Don Jaun

DISCUSSION QUESTIONS

- What is your life goal and do you know the route to take to achieve it?
- What legacy would you like to leave?

INTRODUCTION

Astronomy is a very powerful science, accessible by many, understood by a few. There is evidence to suggest that individuals who have claimed no interest in this powerful science are actually fascinated by the stars and what may be 'out there. I have not come across any formal research that suggests the attraction of astronomy, but this unique attribute may be because it attempts to answer the big questions: the origin of life and the origin of the universe.

Numbers play a central role in our lives. Numbers and number expressions arise early both in hue-man history and in the individual development of us as hue-mans. Numerical notations existed long before the invention of script, and archaeological evidence suggests that at least 30,000 years ago our ancestors used notches as primitive representations for collections of things. In our everyday life, we use numbers in a wide range of different contexts. Numbers also play a role in the spiritual context of many cultures.

Mathematics is defined as the systematic study of nature using symbols to obtain solutions through rigorous deductive reasoning. Meta-mathematics uses mathematics to look beyond mathematics or the thought process.

Unlike Metaphysics, Metha-mathematics is the study of mathematics using mathematical methods. In certain respects, it is closely related to the field of Mathematical logic and propositional Calculus whereby all these fields deal with the mathematical notation of logic and reasoning.

What is it that makes hue-mans numerical beings? What does our concept of numbers encompass? One aspect that comes to mind is cardinality, the property we ask for in 'how many'; for example, I can count the paper clips on my desk and assign them a number. This number assignment allows us not only to distinguish 3 from 4 objects but to also acknowledge the difference between, say, 95 and 96 objects. This method enables us to grasp relations far beyond the limits of perception.

Nature compels us all to keep moving through life. As much as we like to procrastinate, take detours, or even stop. Our development is associated with how we as individuals think. The key to how we apply our thoughts is of supreme importance to each one of us. This knowledge is by means where the evolution on this planet can be uplifted.

Why do some of us seem to attract success, power, wealth, and attainment with very little effort? Others conqueror with great difficulty and many of us fail to meet our ambitions, desires, and ideals? Why is it that some realize their ambitions so easily, others with difficulty and many not at all?

If the cause was physical, the perfect man physically would be the most successful. This suggests that the problem must be mental, it must be in the mind, meaning that the mind is the creative force, which is the sole difference between each of us.

Our minds allow us to overcome our situation, our environment, any obstacles in our path. Once the creative power of thought is understood, its effect becomes visually amazing.

Such results are almost impossible to achieve without access to your code, (the Hue-man Barcode). Knowing your code will give you access to your; patience, diligence, focus and application.

You will then begin to understand that the laws governing you in the mental and spiritual world are as fixed and infallible as those in the material world.

We are at a unique stage in our history. Never have we had such an awareness of what is happening around us and to us, and never have had the power to do something about it and I'm sure things are going to get worse before they get better.

Recently, I've been using the term "down the rabbit hole", a term brought to our attention by renowned author Lewis Carrol, who introduced the term in Alice's Adventures in Wonderland, in 1865.

Today, if someone mentions they went "down the rabbit hole", they generally mean they have been sucked in by some advert or surfing the internet when they should have been studying.

As a metaphor for our condition as first, third, and fourth frequency people, to me, it conveys a sense of time spent in continual transit (four hundred years).

What you are about to read, and access is a meta-mathematical system combined with ancestral astronomy - that was used to understand themselves.

The hue-man code is your blueprint, (system of rules) if you like that guides and manages your path. It's a combination of numbers, symbols, and letters, used to represent who we are, what we are, and what our purpose is. it's a personal barcode assigned to each one of us which only you can unlock.

In modern-day communication systems, information is often both encoded and encrypted. Both sets of codes replace elements of a message with other symbols by a rule defined by a secret key known only to the transmitter (the one who sent you) and the receiver (you). Without this key, a third party cannot invert the replacement to unscramble the cipher (an algorithm for performing encryption or decryption).

During my late teens and early twenties, I always thought of myself as unimportant and unnecessary to the process of understanding truth, to see myself. If we don't understand and merely listen to words, we invariably go away with a series of concepts or ideas, creating a pattern which we then try to implement to adjust our lives.

Do you only listen to what you want to hear? Do you listen through your ambitions, desires, fears, only what will be satisfactory, what gives you comfort, what satisfies you, or what will alleviate your pain? sounds like you are listening to your voice? It's important to not just listen to what is being said but to everything...

To listen to demands that your mind is quiet. When you look at a butterfly, you look not knowing its gender, not naming it, not classifying it, not saying it belongs to a certain species, if you do these things, you cease to look at the butterfly.

Because we are constantly trying to be this or that, to capture a certain experience or avoid another, the mind is constantly occupied with something; if it is never still to listen then how does it hear the noise of its struggle.

Personal development is exactly what it says "Personal". Whether we look backwards or forwards we face puzzling questions: what is the essential nature of our development?

By what purpose does it occur? What factors speed it up and slow it down? What conditions are essential or detrimental to it? Through what stages or phases does it pass through? What are the sources of its problems and its failures? And, most importantly, what is the role of me as a *hue-man* in this development?

There are many reasons why I feel an effort of this nature is both necessary and possible. Presently we are in the worst global financial crisis that expresses the limitations in our present understanding of development. The application of current social and economic theories has produced very disappointing results for us Hue-man. Despite the remarkable developmental achievements of the past forty years, many of us globally remain in poverty by one definition or another.

As light, heat, enzymes, and hormones serve as conducive conditions, catalysts, and reactants for biological processes; peace, democracy, education, unlimited access to technology and information act as conducive conditions, catalysts, and reactants for the social and economic progress of us as a people.

Numbers are basic elements of mathematics that can be used for different operations such as counting, comparing quantities and ranking; number tasks do not involve calculations. In functional magnetic resonance imaging (fMRI) number task studies, stimuli were typically single digits which were later compared to other conditions such as single letters (Eger et al., 2003).

In this meta-analysis, the calculation tasks that utilize mathematical operations, such as subtraction and multiplication, require the subject to identify number quantities and then modify them based on the operational function.

To generate logical answers, mathematical operations generally require numbers to be monitored and manipulated. This is done by using code to convert the numbers to characters - something like ASCII or Unicode - and convert the potentially long infinite text string. Within that text string, you will find infinite character strings which in turn reveals who you are and what your purpose is supposed to be.

DISCUSSION QUESTIONS
- Does a myth hold a stronger truth when it is demystified, or when in its original form?
- Would you prefer to hear scientific justification of the ten plagues or consider them inexplicable miracles?

THE DAWN OF THE 21ST CENTURY

The new millennium has witnessed many new challenges. New challenges naturally demand new approaches, new approaches require new knowledge and skills. Defining and providing quality education in the present knowledge society is not an easy task. Depending on one's interests, passions, talents, and expectations, one can be found in various parts of the globalized world. There is neither one answer that addresses the needs of all.

Putting it bluntly, a new system usually draws upon the historical experience, a colonial and pre-colonial, feudal, and semi-feudal, social, cultural, and intellectual legacy inherited therefrom. In other words, such a system is found to serve the interests of the elite (2nd frequency).

The amazing advancements of knowledge seen in mathematics are based on our inquisitive minds, our powers of investigating and researching the knowledge already out there.

While this may be recognized it is often forgotten that even rudimentary knowledge of this subject would significantly assist our students in other branches of science; thus, reminding us of mathematics' capability to pay its debt to the world...

Among those networks of branches is one significant piece that deals with man's attempt to know thyself. Before we can even attempt to find out who we are and what our purpose is we need to grasp the meaning and phenomena of the universe we find ourselves part of before any form of conditioning to us or the things around us.

The art of Archeoastronomy looks at the study of how people in the past misunderstood the phenomena in the sky, how they used these phenomena and what role the sky played in their culture. Professor Nissen born in Germany (1839 – 1912) was a leading historian and Archeoastronomy of his time. Professor Nissen published many papers on the orientation of ancient temples. Although it had long been known by many that the bases of the pyramids were aligned to the astronomical cardinal points, no one yet suspected that temples also had anything to do with the rising or setting of the sun, moon, or the stars. To a certain extent, the consensus amongst Egyptologists is that the temples of Egypt were simply made to face the Nile.

To obtain a complete picture it is necessary to bring together the information to be obtained from mathematics, and astronomy. It will, I think, become apparent to anyone who reads this book that its limits combined with the current condition of our knowledge can be advanced by using the tools within Mathematics, and Astronomy.

We also need to be clear before we go any further about what the horizon is. The horizon of any place is the circle which bounds our views of the earth's surface, along which the land (or sea) and sky appear to meet.

The aim of this book is designed to serve as an introduction to the topic of accessing 'the hue-man code'. To convey mathematical knowledge and Astronomical information that is usable and applicable. Sharing how the mathematical methods of our ancestors can be used to solve certain misunderstandings not easily solved by other methods. The importance our Ancestors placed on mathematics to solve all problems and establish Truth and Order (ma 'at), apply knowledge to help develop and give understanding for our well-being.

Being a speculative mathematical investigator, nothing is off-limits. There will be no predetermined endpoint, destination, or objective. There will be no well-known hypothesis to prove or disprove; it is the mathematical and astrological exploration itself that is paramount. As there are no boundaries to my inquiry, there is no pressing need to investigate all the boundary conditions. In doing so I hope to add to what came previously while uprooting nothing. The good sense of the reader will determine which numbers are valid – and which are not!!

Assessing our achievements is not the goal, but to ponder the potential and to identify the forces responsible for our achievements and a possible way going forward considering attitude. I would like to believe that many of us the world over would want to live more comfortably, more progressively, and more intelligently.

In bringing this analysis of the hue-man code I have formulated research on ancient, ancestral, teachings, and expanded them based on our specific needs. Accessing research about the celestial plains, combined with over 20 years of personal mathematical study, modelling, and practice.

Our development requires peace of mind, Freedom to express, Education about self, Technology, & Organization. This would allow us to come and work together as a people in a structured manner. Hue-man's working together can achieve more than working alone.

With that said, this book however does not teach mathematics or mathematical concepts, but it does emphasize the importance of mathematics and hopefully provides motivational insight and inspiration into the relationship between Ancient Ancestral mathematics and our hue-man code.

DISCUSSION QUESTIONS
- Are you in love with the "idea" of love?
- Are you happy with your nakedness?
- Does your love have conditions, or is it unconditional?

GENETIC CODE FOR SOCIAL DEVELOPMENT

The Genetic Code for Social Development by: Harlan Cleveland, Garry Jacobs, Robert Macfarlane, Robert Van Harten, N. Asokan stated the following:

The genetic code in DNA molecules governs the release and utilization of energy for biological development. The hue-man choice is the basic mechanism for liberating and productively harnessing the potential energy within. It is the mind's decision that releases human energy and propels it into action, for the purposes preselected by the Hue-man mind Andrzej Sicinski forcefully expressed this perspective: "We live in cultural reality". Our thought processes must consider differences in culture. The cultural dimension is lacking in the paper on Human Choice paper. It is too individualistic and neglects systems of values, systems of ideas and systems of language that differ from culture to culture."

Tony Judge supported this view. "It is arrogant to think that we know how to choose the right model for other societies. We could be making dangerous assumptions that are not valid in practice."

Stanley Kalpage, a chemist from Sri Lanka, sided with the cultural perspective.
"Culture is very important. Science is not the ultimate basis on which we should build development theory."

DISCUSSION QUESTIONS

- Is your affection derived from neediness, or is it given as a gift?
- Are you wholeheartedly giving all the love you have?
- Are you happy with the one you love?
- Do you love someone in order to escape from the problems of life?

THE CODE OF LIFE

E (EVENTS) + R (RESPONSE) = O (OUTCOME)

Think back to a recent episode in which you felt as if you were being true to yourself. How would you describe what you did? Perhaps you would say that you 'trusted your guts' or 'followed your heart', rather than 'thinking with your head'. You might also assume that these idioms involving the guts or the heart belong to an outdated folklore – that they are a poetic rather than a scientific expression of what's happening when we tap into our sense of self. Yet, emerging scientific evidence increasingly suggests that being aware of who you are – being *self-conscious* – really does depend, not just on processes in your brain, but also on what's happening deep in your viscera. It is located within every one of our hue-man cells. It involves perfect cellular health, unrestricted cellular communication, and subsequently, uninhibited DNA replication. The language our cells utilize to communicate with each other, and the immune system is The Hue-man Code of Life.

Our code holds happiness, sadness, dangers and confusion that only you can enjoy, endure, or banish. It is a mystery to access the realms of the ancestors, and the sphere of the inexplicable.

Your code accesses directions, vocations and life paths laid down by the Creator, to help you discover the truths about yourselves.

Everyone - except those who are unaware - knows that mathematics is the general Code of Life. It is more than just numeric numbers, it regulates everything from ceremonies, our daily lives, the health of our bodies, and the rights of individuals.

Your life code is the written instructions with the body. Scripture declares how the creator writes His instructions - teachings in the heart (soul, inner man, Jer.31:31 - 34), many scientists call this part of code as naturally or chemically written in hue-mans DNA. Whether you call it life instructions (the Law) or the adverse effects of the law, which is death. "Figuratively speaking, our code can be described as the recipe book for who and how we are, while epigenetic regulation can be seen as notes that have been penciled into the margins."

Quoting *Knight and Landweber (2000)*: "...In the absence of evidence, many of the most interesting questions about genetic code have fallen into a twilight zone of speculation and controversy. Although it is generally accepted that the modern code evolved from a simpler form, there has not been consensus about when the initial code evolved or what it was like, how and when particular amino acids were added, how and when the modern tRNA/synthetase system arose, or the process by which the code could have expanded..." Hence the importance of using and developing a rigorous, methodological approach when tackling *Code Interpretation*.

DISCUSSION QUESTION

- What is your definition of a code?

- What is a pseudocode question?

- If the answer given to a problem does not resolve the problem, is the answer wrong or has the problem been mis-diagnosed?

CODED JOURNEY

Each week a global thinker from the world of philosophy, science, psychology or of the arts is given a minute to put forward a radical, inspiring, or controversial idea – no matter how improbable-that they believe would change the world.

Elizabeth Moon, who writes about global warming, like many others would like to see everyone implanted with microchips for ease of identification and enforcement. Moon, who has published essays warning of the dire effects of global warming and even made catastrophic global warming part of the background to her novels, made the stunning revelation on *22/05/2012, in a BBC Radio* programme on possible futures. Asked for her version for the future of humanity, *Moon,* stunned and "terrified" the other guests with this version:

"If I were empress of the universe, I would insist on every individual having a unique ID permanently attached – a barcode if you will; an implanted chip to provide an easy, fast, inexpensive way to identify individuals.

It would be imprinted on everyone at birth. Point the scanner at someone and there it is. Anonymity would be impossible as would mistaken identity making it easier to place responsibility accurately, not only in war but also in non-combat situations far from the war."

BBC Future: Barcode Everyone at Birth

Moon's astonishing version for the future reveals the war-mist obsession with the supposed need for tracking and enforcement of personal behaviour. It reveals the fantasies of control and administration of everyday life that seems to motivate many of those whose professed concern is the future of the planet, but whose interests seem to lie in the ever-closer administration of an individual's daily lives. Some time ago the Infowars website detailed some of the proposals that were being floated for controlling people's movements and activities, including carbon rationing and calorie cards whose avowed aim is the curtailment of people's lives in the name of saving the environment.

Given the horrific history of totalitarian states' attempts to dehumanise people by reducing them to mere cyphers numbers in a database, you would think that an author such as *Moon* would show some cultural awareness and be wary of making proposals that disregard the history of such attempts. But it seems that this is not the case.

In revealing her fantasies of being "empress of the universe" and "bar-coding humanity at birth", *Moon* has done us a favour in giving us a glimpse into a mindset that has a global influence on hue-mans that are controlled, governed, and oppressed by 2nd frequency in every region of the world. To give ourselves a chance to evolve, we must dedicate ourselves to the search for the truth "OUR HUE-MAN CODE?"

DISCUSSION QUESTIONS

- What would a moral code of conduct look like to you?
- Which Pan-African activist, prior to his assasination, stated in 1980 that 'One type of struggle we regard as fundamental is ...*the struggle against our own weakness*?

EPIGENETIC CHANGE

*In the book on the evolution of intelligence **"The Dragon of Eden,"** the late Carl Sagan as early as 1977, speculated that most complex organisms on earth today contain substantially more stored information, both genetic and extra-genetic, than most complex organisms of two hundred million years ago. According to Sagan, the basic means for capturing this information lies within something termed "genetic memory".*

Interestingly, Joseph Nadeau, director of scientific development at the institute for system biology in Seattle, has tracked more than one hundred biochemical, physiological and behavioural traits that are affected by epigenetic changes. In addition, he has seen more of these changes passed down through four generations.

Open Access Vol 2; issue 2011:1-22 IIOAB-India

DISCUSSION QUESTIONS

- What do you know about Melanin? And where does it originate from?
- What does Carbon Dioxide mean to you?IN THE BEGINNING

At the age of 15, I was told by a (2nd frequency) careers officer that I would not amount to much and I should get a job driving the buses. The height limit was 5ft 3in. I was already 5ft 7in. After leaving school I self-studied mathematics for 5yrs and ended up with a degree in Computer science. It was only then I felt as if I had found myself. I went on to study electronics and music. Music is not only an art and therapeutic but also a practical occupation, which makes it important.

As far as I can remember mathematics has always been a refuge when everything around seemed confusing. As a student, I enjoyed maths even though the teaching was poor. It was the one subject where the teacher couldn't criticize with subjective opinion. Either one is correct or is not and it is provable! Maths has always provided the truth when everything else obscures the truth. Mathematics has allowed me to feel comfortable about who I am...

Looking back through the crystal ball of time is nostalgic. I smile remembering my first steps in mathematics, so clumsy and incommensurable to my greater ambitions. You dig even further back and there they are - the roots of the real beginning, the two "chances" and events that preprogrammed my future interest and development. I was probably 8 at the time when a family member, intrigued by my attempts at solving maths problems older than my age group, presented me with a collection of maths magazines. This transformed my childhood. I began deriving equations in the same manner as boys older than me (I went to an all-boys school). Mathematics was my favourite subject, teaching me to strategize, to look into problems in their entirety, something that later on has proved to be an asset in planning and completing research projects, etc… In those days, even though I had to attend church, for me there was very little room for religion, it was mathematics that became my religion. After graduating I worked for several years in the financial sector, moving from one private-sector firm to another until I landed a job in the education sector teaching mathematics. I spent a good deal of my evenings sifting through mathematical books, preparing notes. Even though I felt I had landed my dream job there was not the spark that I was expecting, the spark I imagined was not there. It wasn't until sometime after, I had a visit from my mother who has passed over to the ancestors, telling me that you are in the right vocation but the wrong system. You must do it for yourself by helping others. My mother disappeared as quickly as she appeared. The next day without hesitation I went to work, handed in my notice, my badge, entrance pass and left that building never to return. Since then I have set up my own maths tutoring company, teaching mathematics and science, which has allowed me to expand my vocation and apply my skills to the lives and betterment of others.

Making bad decisions in our daily lives is costly, it causes us to lose time, money, happiness, relationships and even our health can suffer. If what you believe is based on false information, you make bad decisions that affect our lives, professionally and personally. Because of certain conditioning, you may find it difficult to let go of a certain belief, it's not easy. The consequences of false understanding have been researched and show that flawed thinking, behaviour patterns and feelings: are what the scientific literature calls cognitive biases. (scientifliterature.org)

Since pursuing my journey and investigating mathematics, what has surprised me exponentially is how many bad decisions we make as hue-mans stem from false information and misunderstanding. When engaging with the news or any kind of social media, it's important to remember these things before forming opinions on what you have just heard/read/seen.

Statistics can be easily presented in such a way as to "prove" whatever the writer wants them to prove. This is particularly true when it comes to percentages. I see this often when reading progressive-slanted stories about the growth of very small groups, like atheists or transgender people.
A 50% increase over five years sounds impressive until you realize that a 50% increase in a small number is still a small number, overall.

Poll questions can be asked in such a way as to get the desired response. Not just the wording of the question itself, but the person asking it, can change the respondent's response. Similarly, a non-trivial number of non-voting Hue-man's (including me) do not respond to poll questions anymore, because we believe the pollsters are biased.

Opinion poll questions assume that the responder had an opinion before being asked the question, and that opinion was important to them. "I don't know" or "I don't care" aren't always presented as options. Or the responder may not be comfortable saying that they don't care about a "hot button" issue.

It is easy, particularly with social media and the internet, to find whatever you need to "prove" the point you're trying to make. Including Statistics and facts that "prove" your point, Quotes from people who support your point, Anecdotes from people that push your narrative.

I was reminded of this recently when I read a story online. It looked like a professional recent kind of story. The gist of it was about how white people like dogs so much because dogs fill the role that minorities used to fill: the need for white people to have something subservient to them that they can both care for and control.

Someone said that on Twitter, and some other people responded to it, and, the next thing you know, there's an entire story about how this "controversy" had "blown up" and "gone viral" and everyone was "getting triggered."

There were, at best, about 10,000 people who even read the initial Tweet, and maybe about 100 people who responded to it. But, sure enough, some of those responses "proved" the exact narrative the author was trying to prove when they began writing the story, so they were included in it.

There is no set bar for calling something "viral" or "controversial." You can set that bar as low as you want to prove whatever point you want to prove, and someone will always jump over it, right into your chosen narrative. For centuries we have limited ourselves to given facts that often have not been verified. Nothing much has changed since then, apart from a different set of hypotheses, that keep us in the same situation.

Detail of the method used to produce an idea is the basis for judging a work of art, the same is true with Mathematics. The classification of who the 2nd frequency thinks we are, have limited us until now.

DISCUSSION QUESTIONS

- Are you friends with yourself? If so, how do you prove it?
- Do you put your needs and desires last? If so, how does it affect you?

HISTORY OF NUMBERS

In a world divided by culture, politics, religion and race, it is a relief to know one thing that stands above them - mathematics. Cold logic is immune to prejudice, whim and historical atrocities. And yet, through-out history, our ancestors have distilled the essence of the cosmos to capture the magic of numbers in many ways. Too little has been written on the mathematical contribution of our culture. One reason for the neglect of ancestral mathematics was Eurocentrism - British colonial historians paid it little attention, assuming that our ancestors had been too preoccupied with spiritual matters to make significant contributions to the subject. Surviving papyrus texts reveal a rich tradition of ancestral mathematical discoveries dating back to 1550 - 1560 BC. A system of numbers was already established in Africa, together with rules for arithmetical operations and geometry. These were encoded in a complex system of chants, prayers, hymns, curses, charms and other spiritual rituals.

Many thousands of years ago, before writing, literacy or numerical symbols, our ancestors (females) had to manage their menstrual cycle, making them the first hue-man mathematicians. As time passed the men had to tend to their flock, keep track of their cattle. As the agricultural societies developed, mathematical problems emerged in response to the need to measure and divide the land, keep track of livestock, record their harvests, financial transactions and such. With growing populations and clashing cultures came conflict, requiring armies to face the logistics of arming and feeding their soldiers.

Our ancestors began with a system that used symbols for powers of 60 (1, 60, 3600 …), 60 being the smallest number that can be divided evenly by 2, 3, 4, 5, and 6. During the 2nd millennium B.C.E, our ancestors developed a positional system; by 300 B.C.E., they had a symbol for zero as a place holder. The famous Rhind Papyrus (c 1650 B.C.E.) contains many calculations and includes hieroglyphs for addition and subtraction.

Numbers were not only important tools in early civilisations. But they also were a source of mystery and spirituality. Once numbers were named, we became curious about studying numbers. In Babylonia, 60 was the number of Anu, the god of heaven, and 30 was the number of Sin, the lunar god. Many modern religions specify the number of prayers to be recited. In Islam, the number 5 is a good omen. The number 4 is avoided in Japan because of the word for 4. "Shi" sounds like the Japanese word for death. In many cultures today, a well-known superstition surrounds the number 13. The ancestral brotherhood believed that natural numbers were basic to all quantities of matter and living things.

As time passed studies were kept secret, passing down beliefs and results in the oral traditions. A rigid caste and class system hierarchy reserved the mystery of numbers for the elite. The aim was to maintain personal power, mathematical knowledge was a jealously guarded secret. Research tells us that in the Indian culture mathematical communication was deliberately made difficult, such as in the perplexing rhythmic chants of mathematician Aryabhatta in the fifth century AD: It was a recital of values of sine differences in arc minutes which would be memorized by aspiring mathematicians at that time.

Since mathematics is the methodological foundation of hue-man understanding, the geometry of symbols used to express and represent any mathematical concept could and should be cherished, revered, and considered sacred..

1. Monad, Unity, the generator of all numbers and the number of reasons.

2. Dyad, diversity + opinion, the first female number.

3. Triad, harmony = diversity + unity, the first male number.

4, Tetrad, justice or retribution, as in the squaring of accounts "or "let's get this issue squared away".

5. Pentad, marriage (2 + 3 = female + male).

6. Hexad, creation, the articulation of the universe (possibly because $6 = 3 + 2 + 1$).

7. Heptad, perfection, security, safety and rest. The number of laws.

8. Ogdoad, harmony and balance, abundance and power. Known to some to represent the 'Vesica Piscis'

(The Womb of the Universe).

9. Ennead, completion and fulfilment. The 9 is the perfect square, for it contains all the numbers. In this

way all squares become divisible into two triangles since 4 is $1 + 3$, and 9 is $3 + 6$; etc.

All the numbers from 10 upwards, are compound numbers. They have a meaning that is distinct from the root number. It cannot be said with certainty, when and how or at what age these compound numbers were discovered. It can only be said that they appear to have always existed

10. Tetractys represents the four elements of the universe: fire, water, earth, and air, geometrically

Tetractys was represented by 1 dot arranged in an equilateral triangle; arithmetically,

$10 = 1 + 2 + 3 + 4$ (an example of a triangular number).

A perfect number is one that equals the sum of its proper divisors. The number 6 is perfect because

$6 = 1 + 2 + 3$. 28 is also a perfect number because $28 = 1 + 2 + 4 + 7 + 14$.

The number 10, however, is not perfect because $10 \neq 1 + 2 + 5$. Many questions remain about perfect numbers.

The numbers 220 and 284 are amicable because the proper divisors of 220 are 1, 2, 4, 5, 10, 11, 44, 55, 70, 77, and 110, which sum to 284. The proper divisors of 284 are 1, 2, 4, 71, and 142, which sum to 220.

DISCUSSION QUESTION

- What does Ujamaa mean to you?
- Is affirmative actions racist?

Pi (π)

The most famous and important symbol/number in hue-man history and our universe is (pi). The origin is not known for certain, but we do know that the Babylonians approximated in base 60 around 1800 B.C.E. This constant helps us understand our universe with greater clarity. The definition of inspired the notion of a new unit to measure angles. This important angle measure is known as the radian measure and gave rise to many insights into the physical world.

When we compare the length of the circumference of a circle to its diameter, we discover that the circumference is slightly greater than three times the diameter. The number is defined to equal the ratio of the circumference of any circle to its diameter. The ratio is constant no matter the size of the circle. The first 30 digits in the decimal expansion air are 3.141592653589793238462643383279. In 1800 B.C.E our ancestors approximated $= 25 \div 8 = 3.125$. The and e(exponential) signs have enabled us to understand our universe more deeply.

DISCUSSION QUESTIONS

- Can someone have a meaningful life if their life is totally Predetermined?
- Are you able to disentangle morality from meaningfulness?
- Is 'meaning' constituted by the mind?

The Zodiac of Dendera

The original zodiac was in the ceiling of an observatory in the temple of Dendera. This work of art was 'rediscovered' by Napoleon's troops during an expedition to Egypt on 25th May 1799, and then dynamited from the ceiling. This fine piece of African art work, were recognizable astrological symbols which the French explorers anticipated would be the key to unravel ancestral secrets. The African Sky-map is a carved bas-relief in sandstone measuring 2.5 meters square.

The inner circle of figures, which move counter-clockwise like the stars, shows the astronomical signs of the zodiac circling the North Pole, which is symbolised by the jackal. The outer circle of figures represents the 36 decans, each one symbolising the ten-day weeks of the Kemetic year. The twelve figures outside of the circle represent the twelve months of the year and their arms, the 24 hours of the day.

It was sold to Louis XVIII for 150,000 francs and is now located in the Louvre Museum. Since the Louvre acquired the Dendera Zodiac in 1919, the artefact has been the most popular visitor attraction in the section of Egyptian antiques.

Imhotep's ancestors had already constructed their very accurate Solar and Siriac Calendar that showed the exact time the earth took to revolve around the sun and the sun took to revolve around the central Star Sirius. They had already mapped the zodiac, their knowledge of the earth, its measurements, elements, and properties which were expanding rapidly. In fact, Imhotep was born into an age very much like the current one where Science and Technology was expanding at a rapid rate.

If we define astronomy as measuring the heavenly motions and astrology as applying the influence of the observed stars, then both activities were basic requirements in the celestial religion that our ancient ancestors practiced.

DISCUSSION QUESTIONS

- Do you mostly live in the past, present, or future?
- What are the things you do to stimulate your mind?
- Is it racist to be blind to colour?

EMPIRICAL DATA (X) MATHEMATICS

It is important to understand the relationship that exists between the astrological signs of the zodiac and mathematics.

Gaining knowledge of ourselves is not taught in public schools but it must be our priority as a people. We always encourage our children to go to school and to know the value of education because we know they are the future, and the future depends on our youth. Once you know who you are and where you come from no one can take that away from you.

Mathematics is a fundamental component of who we are. It is an intellectual and scientific tool created by African people to systematically study, learn, and comprehend nature.

Know yourself – anyone who does not know and doesn't even know they don't know is foolish – disregard them. A person who doesn't know but knows they don't know – is teachable.

A person who does not know but believes they do know is dangerous – avoid them. A person who knows but does not know they know is very wise – follow them. Every one of these personas resides in you. Know thyself and Maat be true.

A modern adaptation of an ancient proverb

DECIPHERING

A code is a set of laws or regulations, a set of rules about how to behave, a set of letters, numbers, symbols, etc., that is used to secretly send messages to someone.

The purpose of a code is: to put a message into the form of a code so that it can be kept secret so that it can be identified so that you can change (information) into a set of letters, numbers, or symbols so that the message can be translated (interpreted).

The definition of code has also been defined as "a mapping between the objects of two independent worlds that is implemented by the objects of the third world called adaptors"
(Barbieri, 2003).

Numbers are the law of the universe. As travellers on the journey of life, we all move at varying speeds. Many have stopped for too long; others are resting, and many have taken detours. Not fulfilling your primary goal (your purpose). Knowing your ruling number guides you through your life path, aligns you with your passion, matching you with your rightful vocation.

In bringing this researched analysis of sacred numbers I have formulated my research on ancient, ancestral, teachings, and have expanded it based on our specific needs as a people using research about the celestial plains combined with over 25 years of personal mathematical study, research, and practice.

Each one of us as hue-man has a unique ID permanently attached – a barcode if you will. It is the numerical numbers that represent your capabilities and hold the number key to your existence. It is the code to who you are, where you belong, your purpose in life and so much more.

Knowing your b-code guides you through life's path, aligns you with your passion, matching you with your correct vocation. In bringing you his analysis I formulated this research on our Ancestral knowledge and expanded that knowledge based on our needs as Hue man. It was also important to research the Celestial plains combined with personal mathematical study, knowledge, and practice which I am now sharing with you.

What is a codon – it is a sequence of three DNA or RNA nucleotides that correspond with a specific amino acid or stop signal during protein synthesis. Each codon corresponds to a single amino acid (or stop signal), and the full set of codons is called the genetic code. Our Ancestors similarly viewed mathematics. Obtaining the correct knowledge is the key to knowing all secrets and all mysteries. In mathematics, a mystery is an unknown (x).

Using mathematics allows the mind to be able to go from one reasonable, sensible, accurate, step after another to solve a problem. Mathematical concepts can be traced back to the prime source origin of mathematics which is the African continent and our ancestor's minds.

Each person's purpose is given to them before they are even born. I, for example, chose to work with mathematics, to explore the mysteries that are shrouded in numbers and signs, to explore many of the hidden unknown. Allowing myself to be consumed by these mysteries so that others might learn. I made a self-commitment to venture to unknown areas so that one day in the future others would be able to see into the unknown and know.

Your code has been given to you as a means of tapping into the cosmic intelligence and extracting from it your dreams, desires, ambitions, and aspirations. Everything around us was once someone's thought, thought, therefore, is constructive. Our thought is the spirit of the cosmos operating through us as a people. Your b-code instructs you how to use that power, using it both constructively and creatively. This tells us that the things and conditions we desire to become reality must first be created in thought. Our *code* will explain and guide you through the process. It will also equip you with a greater personality, a worthy purpose, and a new ability to enjoy life's beauty and wonders.

Each number is a carrier of information. Each number stands for meanings beyond the apparent ones, and ratios indicate geometry. Mathematics is the science of science. It is the combination of mathematics based on the evidence and the scientific methods that enable the correct and accurate description of our *code*.

Being able to decode your code, the ability to replicate, model, manipulate, and control various aspects of nature using mathematics was known to our African ancestors as Heka. Heka as a concept was often defined as magic, today it would be classed as engineering, which is defined as "the process of acquiring and applying scientific and mathematical knowledge to design and develop inventions that realise a desired objective. It is interesting to note that the etymology of the word engineer comes from the word "engine" meaning "skill and cleverness" and the word "Ingenium" meaning "inborn qualities or talent `` and gene "meaning" to beget or produce.

DISCUSSION QUESTIONS
- Do you spend enough time by yourself?
- What three issues can you reflect on in solitude?
- Do you have friends that you don't like to spend more than 30 minutes with? If so, why?

THE POWER OF 2

From 0 – 9, the name of numbers and the mathematical values of the numbers have a great place in African culture. All numbers except for numerical zero (0) originated in Africa.

The rising generation should learn how the names and numbers were depicted on stone monuments as a means of communicating while returning to ancestral ancient periods (hieroglyphics). These numbers have not only concrete but also abstract cultural value in the African thought system. The numbers are both universal and international. The names of the numbers hold the belief of our ancestors that geometry and mathematics (numbers) share the same concept.

The oldest numbering system found in Africa was the Binary base-2 numbering system. This numbering system can also be used to indicate quantities using tone, rhythm, and light. As this system only needs two indicators to specify a quantity, the basis of music which is a beat and a rest can be used as a method of conveying binary data.

DISCUSSION QUESTIONS
- What do you base your personal happiness on?

- Do you pursue happiness, or do you live in joy and appreciation of the present moment?

MORSE CODE

Morse Code is a basic, widely known system of using just "dots" and "dashes" to communicate. It was first developed by Samuel Morse in 1836 to fill the need for a faster long-distance form of communication. The simplicity of the method cemented its place and use within history, and it still can be employed in a wide spectrum of scenarios today. Because of the minimalistic form of Morse code, it can be tailored to fit the communication needs of different people by using a variety of methods.

The invention of the Morse Code was attributed to Samuel F. B. Morse; however, the concept of using sound, tone, rhythm, and light to convey information has been done in Africa for centuries.

The binary base-2 system used to develop Morse code has also served as the inspiration to develop the barcode for international delivery companies like (DHL).

Our Ancestors formulated and used a binary-base 2 numbering system. This system could be used to indicate quantities using tone, rhythm, and light.

Morse code is a rhythmic signal similar to music which is a Beat and a Rest that can be used to convey binary data. Morse Code communicates letters and numbers on a telegraph to send messages.

The invention of the Morse Code was attributed to Samuel F. B. Morse even though this practice had been carried out by our ancestors in Africa for centuries. The etymology dictionary states that "Morse" is dark-skinned, Moorish, which indicates that the concept originated with our ancestors in Africa.

In 1999, the Morse code was discontinued as the international standard for maritime distress calls. In 2007, the FCC removed knowing Morse code as a requirement for getting an amateur radio license.

African Creation Energy

DISCUSSION QUESTION
- Are you comfortable within or are you fitting in?
- Do you find your self-worth from yourself, or do you base it on the opinions of others?

BARCODE

All barcodes look pretty much similar. They have the same alternating black and white lines.

Originally barcodes were designed to identify moving rail cars and their cargo and destination. Now they are widely used for product inventory and serial number tracking. The most universal one is the UPC code which is used by most manufacturers and retail stores to track inventory.

The UPC barcode as designed in 1973 was coincidently designed around the number 666. Universal Product Codes or UPCs are found on almost every product today. These codes allow the cashier to scan the items into the computer instead of entering the price manually. UPC is made up of numbers and bars, the bars themselves also have numerical values. If you notice on any barcode the bars on the left in the middle and on the right of the code have no numerical numbers beneath them however the other bars all do. So by comparing these three bars at the beginning, the middle and end with numbered bars it is clear that those dividing bars always represent the number six. Even though it may not be apparently visible to anyone who looks at it, there is a mathematical representation thereof the number 666.

The book of Revelation tells us that in the last few days no one will be able to buy or to sell without the number 666. Contrary to industry insiders who claim it is all a coincidence the fact remains that virtually all products sold globally are sold with the number 666 built into them.

The very first number decides the type of product – standard, weighted item, pharmacy, coupons etc.

The first five sets of numbers tell you who the manufacturer of the product is.

The next five sets of numbers tell the product code.

The final digit is called Modulo check character. It is used for error checking.

Identification Number | Item Number | Check Digit

QUANTUM CODE

Quantum code is the hidden intelligent design that gives the standard model of Particle physics symmetry and supersymmetry. DNA is a code inside hue-man matter or cells which scientists can see unravel manifesting in every hue-man. DNA and RNA are future chains in a link that receive energy and information from quantum code assembly. They are the cart after the Quantum Code which is the real horse in front, controlling and directing the course of a hue-mans journey in life.

Dr Mukesh Chauhan

THE HUE-MAN CODE

The hue-man code is the written instruction within the body. Scriptures declare how the creator writes His instructions - teachings in the heart (soul of inner man, Jer.31:31 - 34), researchers or scientists call this part of the code as naturally or chemically written in hue-mans DNA, not in stone. Whether it be life instructions (LAW) or the adverse effect of the Law, which is death (the reverse effect of the Law), hue-manity activates one of the two powers in the body according to the Law's instructions. It is possible to turn on and off one of the two powers (Deut. 30:19). The more hue-manity obeys the word of the creator, the hue-man code will take over and pass it to the generations on the reverse side.

The instructions that one carries can utterly change the DNA of another person in transfusion or any treatment unless the host person's code is more powerful than the new object that is transmitted to the body (Mark. 16:18).

Seblewongel Wolde 2021

DISCUSSION QUESTION

- What is the difference between a code and a formula?
- How well do you deal with criticism?

ASTRONOMY Vs ASTROLOGY

The cosmos works in mysterious ways. It is constantly working to make available to you the tools, resources, people, and the lessons you need to become the person you were meant to be. But it doesn't always make these things obvious (so we think).

Using your b-code, you can recognize when the universe is trying to tell you something or lead you in the direction you should be going.

Astrology is related to Mathematics as it relies on the use of charts to determine the signs in the universe. However, to construct those charts, astrology uses a lot of mathematics. Each zodiac sign marks the amount of space the sun moves from the viewpoint of the earth, in the amount of time it takes to complete one moon orbit.

Astronomy is also related to Mathematics – Mathematics ok's the findings in astronomy. Mathematics has supervisory control over research in astronomy. All orbital characteristics are Pi-related and, therefore, they are transcendental numbers. The use of continued fractions for approximation using polynomials et al in astronomy is certainly relevant. Using Precession of the Ages as a Timeline for Future History.

DISCUSSION QUESTIONS

- What are the ten planets looked at in the study of Astrology?
- How do you perceive pain?

EQUINOX

As there is no consensus as to when the age of Aquarius begins there are several suggested approximation dates for entering the Age of Aquarius, for example, from 1447 A.D to 3597 A.D.

Nicholas Champion, 'Book of the world'

The Precession of the Equinoxes: (The 'Platonic Year'...)
It has been observed that certain ancient myths, sacred texts, and ancient buildings have a code (ï¿½storedï¿½) within them, common and repeating numerical values and dimensions which relate to astronomical phenomena.

What is Precession:
The precession of the equinoxes refers to the observable phenomena of the rotation of the heavens, a cycle which spans a period of (approximately) 25,920 years, over which time the constellations appear to slowly rotate around the earth, taking turns at rising behind the rising sun on the vernal equinox.
This remarkable cycle is due to synchronicity between the speed of the earth's rotation around the sun, and the speed of rotation of our galaxy.

The Precession of the equinoxes = 25,920 yrs. = (360ï¿½ rotation)
If the sky is divided into 12 constellations:

(25,920 / 12 = 2,160)

(Note: 6 x 10 x 6 = 360 and 360 x 6 = 2,160)

A New sign appears on the horizon every 2,160 yrs. (30ï¿½).

Note: (2 x 2,160 or 12 x 360 = 4,320 yrs.).

Therefore, to move 1ï¿½ on the horizon = 72 yrs. (approx.).

The following numbers can therefore be regarded as processionary:

(12 ... 30 ... 72 ... 360 ... 2,160 ... 4,320 and 25,920).

It is now suggested that at some point in the distant past this cycle was determined by astronomers (A process requiring the prolonged and precise observation of the equinoctial conjunction of the rising sun and the 'suns carrier' behind).

Such a discovery goes a long way to understanding the prehistoric fascination with astronomy and the apparent 'will move mountains' exhibited by the builders of many megalithic monuments. Lockyer observed that prehistoric astronomy was started on the horizon, which would go a long way towards explaining the early development of the English structures called 'Henges', with their built-up banks creating excellent artificial horizons.

The Processionary cycle is measured in 'months' named according to the constellation visible behind the vernal equinox sunrise. We are presently finishing the 'age of Pisces' and will be soon entering the 'age of Aquarius'. It is suggested (and supported by a growing weight of evidence), that this cycle was recognised at least as far back as the age of Taurus, although there are suggestions of recognition as far back as Leo (as represented by the Sphinx at Giza).

The Equinoctial Gnomon Method is simply the African circle method used on the equinox. On the equinox, the surveyor will find that the tip of the shadow runs in a straight line and nearly perfectly east-west. Since the shadow line is already straight and already runs east-west, the second step in the solar gnomon method, drawing a circle around the gnomon, is not required. Our ancestors were able to establish the day of the equinox by observing the solstice and counting forward 91 days. This is a method our ancestors may have used to align the pyramids. It produces results that match the alignments of the largest pyramids of the pyramid age in magnitude and direction.

The Journal of Ancient African Architecture - vol. 2, 2017

illustration by Wilma Wetterstrom

NUMEROLOGY

I have read a number of books on numerology and compared texts. The majority of them seem to agree on the basic meaning of numbers and how they apply to earth dates. During my research I noticed that those books that were underpinned by mathematics certainly had more depth allowing further verification of accuracy. For me the understanding of the basic meaning of numbers alone is not enough. The study of numbers puts one on the road to illumination. A whole new world will open up for you if you are sincerely seeking answers.

Numerology is a set of ideas, beliefs, or hypotheses about the relationship between numbers and reality. There is nothing wrong or incorrect about forming hypotheses and beliefs, however, when conclusions are drawn about the hypothesis and beliefs without appropriately testing them using astrological or mathematical methods leads to inaccurate explanations of reality that cannot be used. It can neither be accurately applied and wastes time, energy, and effort of the individuals who have accepted the inaccurate explanation as truth and have attempted to apply them without any success.

In the world of numerology, from my understanding there seems to be two avenues of thought to follow. One is to concentrate on finding and experimenting with new combinations of numbers and letters in search of understanding, which many seem to be doing or have done. The other avenue is researching, contemplating, and meditating on symbolic meanings and the extended meanings of numbers which is done less often. It's important to note that when we meditate on any particular number, shape or symbol it will reveal itself. It's important to appreciate that symbols and numbers are the universal language of the soul.

Numbers never fail. Numbers, believe it or not, are law. There is nothing made that does not have size, shape and dimension. If you study or research an atom you will find the key to the functioning of the hue-man. Atoms are the basic building blocks from which everything around us is built. This includes the computer before you, the floor beneath you, the air you breathe, and the stars you see at night. All of them are made up of atoms. Every element has its own pattern that never varies ""As above So below".
Even though we cannot see these molecules of energy with the naked eye, they nevertheless still exist.

We all enter this world at a certain date, hour, a minute into the earth's energy field. The vibrations and conditions of that energy field must determine to a great extent the particular actions and reactions that will characterise our whole lives. Once we take our first breath we are conditioned by the basic set of vibrations that were active at that precise moment. What separates mathematics from numerology is the presence of rigorous deductive reasoning and consistency.

My view is that our code represents universal principles through which things evolve and continue to grow cyclically. I also believe that every word, name, or title vibrates to a number and every number has an inner meaning. Even disease has a distinct vibration. An American physician, Dr Abrams, invented an instrument to measure all of the reactions to the human body and was able to assign a numerical value to each disease. Dr Abrams believed the remedy could also be figured out through numbers *(The finding of the third eye, 114)*. Many of the studies I have come across suggest to me that the source of all colour, sound, and vibration belongs to the spiritual plane, and not the physical. As above, So below"

As hue-mans, our name, language, culture, family unit, spirituality, sanity and life was ripped away from us and we were indoctrinated with names, languages, religions, and cultures, alien to our way of being.

Is it not a fact that culture is something that you cannot see or touch, thereby making it abstract. Culture only exists in the minds of people, and it portrays itself through the habits of people. It practically affects people's way of thinking and the ways people do things. If our culture has been distorted then who are we?

Culture is the invisible bond which ties people together. It refers to the pattern of human activity. The art, literature, language, and religion of a community represent its culture. Our cultural values and beliefs manifest themselves through our lifestyle.

Our moral values represent our culture. The importance of culture lies in its close association with the ways of thinking and living. Differences in cultures have led to a diversity in the people from different parts of the world.

Our culture is related to the development of our attitude. Our cultural values influence how we approach living. According to the behaviorist definition of culture, it is the ultimate system of social control where people monitor their own standards and behavior. Our cultural values are supposed to serve as the founding principles of our life. They shape our thinking, behavior, and personality.

As travelers on the journey of life, we all move at varying speeds. Many have stopped for far too long, others are resting, and many have taken detours, not fulfilling their primary goal, (the distortion of culture, spirituality and language has hampered our condition).

It is better to be silent, or say a few things that have more value than silence. learn the art of saying a few words meaning a lot rather than saying a lot and meaning very little.

It is the simple hypotheses of which one must be most wary; because these are the ones that have most chances of passing unnoticed.

Poincaré

DISCUSSION QUESTIONS

- What came first, numbers or vibrations?
- Do you accept pain as a natural part of life?
- What lessons have pain taught you that you can pass on to benefit others?

KEMETIC FORMULA

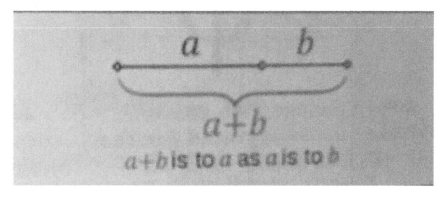

Known as the Golden Ratio it can be used to mathematically show growth and creation, it can also be used to demonstrate the natural mathematics of destruction. Expressed in Ancient Africa by the Axiom: "*As Above, So Below*"

The symbol is a conventional representation. The hieroglyph is direct, nonconventional writing, and only a hieroglyph is able directly to transcribe the intelligence-of-the-heart and be translated thereafter by the cerebral intelligence.

Any other method of esoteric writing either requires the elimination of much of the grammatical form—leaving it to the reader to gather the meaning of the words without imposing a frame of reference—or else resorts to devices such as allegory, metaphor, parable, play on words, or phonetic cabalism. The synchronicity of the universe is determined by certain mathematical constants which express themselves in the form of 'patterns' and 'cycles' in nature.

DISCUSSION QUESTIONS
- Name a positive ratio in your life?
- What metaphor would you use to describe yourself?

RATIO TRANSPARENCY

"The Golden Number is a mathematical definition of a proportional function which all of nature obeys, whether it be a mollusc shell, the leaves of plants, the proportions of the animal body, the human skeleton, or the ages of growth in man."

— *R.A. Schwaller de Lubicz, Nature Word*

"Highly complex numbers like the Comma of Pythagoras, Pi and Phi (sometimes called the Golden Proportion), are known as irrational numbers. They lie deep in the structure of the physical universe and were seen by the Egyptians as the principles controlling creation, the principles by which matter is precipitated from the cosmic mind.

Today scientists recognize the Comma of Pythagoras, Pi and the Golden Proportion as well as the closely related Fibonacci sequence are universal constants that describe complex patterns in astronomy, music and physics. ...

To the Egyptians, these numbers were the secret harmonies of the cosmos and they incorporated them as rhythms and proportions in the construction of their pyramids and temples."

— *Jonathan Black, Mark Booth*

"The conclusion that the Egyptians of the Old Kingdom were acquainted with both the Fibonacci series and the Golden Section, says *Stecchini*, is so startling concerning current assumptions about the level of Egyptian mathematics that it could hardly have been accepted based on Herodotus' statement alone, or on the fact that the phi [golden] proportion happens to be incorporated in the Great Pyramid.

But the many measurements made by Professor Jean Philippe Lauer, says Stecchini, definitely prove the occurrence of the Golden Section throughout the architecture of the Old Kingdom... Schwaller de Lubicz also found graphic evidence that the pharaonic Egyptians had worked out a direct relation between pi and phi in that $pi = phi^2 \times 6/5$."

Peter Tompkins, <u>Secrets of the Great Pyramid:</u>

THE NATURAL WORLD

Displays of mathematical and geometric constants are confirmation that certain proportions are woven into the very fabric of nature. Recognising the significance of this simple fact offers us the means to understand how and why such matters were considered sacred. They and everything around us, are the product of the delicate balance between chaos and order.

The word 'geometry' can be traced through its parts:

The word 'Geo-metry' comes from the Greek words Geos meaning 'Earth' and Metron meaning 'To measure', which together literally translate as the 'Measuring of the earth' or 'Earthly measurements', an art used by our ancestors which was thereafter restricted to the priesthood.

Sacred geometry has existed in many forms across the ages. It is often mistakenly said that geometry began with the Greeks, but before they were the Minoans, the Egyptians, Sumerians, Indus valley, Chinese, Phoenicians and of course, the builders of the western European megaliths all of whom left clear geometric fingerprints in their greatest constructions. The Greeks may well have been the first to have offered geometry to the public at large, but they were by no means the first to realise it.

Sacred-Geometry:

One of the most common shapes in nature is the circle, it is therefore extremely significant to understand that all other geometric shapes can be determined from a circle...with the use of only a compass (or string) and a ruler (straight edge)

Geometry and mathematics exist in their ideal world. When we draw a circle on a piece of paper this is not the real circle, the real circle is in that world, and this is just an approximation of the real circle and the same with all the other sacred shapes.

There are five platonic solids assigned to the elements that form the world.

When the term 'sacred' is used, it does not mean that we should fall on our knees, bow, pray, or start meditating. Sacred, in the definition sense of the word, is something requiring appreciation and should be greatly valued. Sacred geometry begins with the logical beginning of everything which is nothing. Before there was something there was nothing.

The first thing that came into existence was a point. Before anything can be, it must start with a point. A point occupies no space, it has no dimensions, it's so small it can't be moved or measured. Yet it encompasses everything within it. You could say this point is spirit and what is the first thing that spirit does, it becomes conscious, it becomes 360 degrees of awareness in the vast emptiness of void.

Our ancient ancestors believed that this innate aspect of consciousness is what sparked the process of creation, then what did spirit do? The only thing it could do, it moved.

From the vantage point of pure mathematics motion is impossible in a void. You can't go anywhere, rotate, or fall, there is just infinite emptiness in all directions. So in order to move you need something in relation to move too. Before there was light there was movement, once spirit created a point in space it was able to move to the edge of its awareness and expand consciousness creating another circle to form the Vesica Pisces. This oval shaped opening in the middle is the geometric image through which light was created and it is also the geometric shape through which our eyes receive light..

DISCUSSION QUESTIONS

- Are you prepared to face death?
- Does your perception of death impact the way you live your life?

GEOMETRIC (SACRED) SHAPES

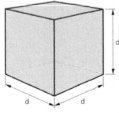

Earth, Cube = 8 Vertices, 12 Edges, 6 Faces, Each with 4 sides.

Fire, Tetrahedron = 4 Vertices, 6 Edges, 4 Faces, Each with 3 sides.

Air, Octahedron = 6 Vertices, 12 Edges, 3 Faces, Each with 3 sides.

 Icosahedron, Water = 12 Vertices, 30 Edges, 20 Faces, Each with 3 sides.

 Dodecahedron, Universe = 20 Vertices, 30 Edges, 12 Faces, Each with 5 sides.

THE LANGUAGE OF THE UNIVERSE

The original African numbering system (as old as 4000 BC) is a combination of binary mathematics, Geometry, and spirituality, that seeks to solve problems and answer questions. To access the truth.

Throughout history, numbers have come to mean different things to different people, cultures, and faiths. Nonetheless, numbers have been given similar meanings. Any developments after would have been inspired and motivated by the original system.

Numbers 1-9, (0) being a placeholder, have universal principles. On a personal level, they stand for characteristics, abilities, and events. On a mathematical level, these numbers are used for the art of counting, measuring, coding, ordering, labelling and qualification.

Synchronicity and the meaning of numbers are all extremely personal so beware of prescribing meaning to your life that is not correct or relevant. Not doing any research and just going with the flow or what the traditional meaning of the number is can be more detrimental than useful. Do your research to see what numbers mean for you primarily.

It is important to emphasize that while it is beneficial to find out the general meaning of numbers it is imperative to understand a number mathematically.

Your code has been given to you as a means of tapping into the cosmic intelligence and attracting from it your dreams and aspirations. Everything around us was once someone's thought, thought, therefore, is constructive. Human thought is the spirit of the cosmos operating through us as a people. Your b-code instructs you how to use that power, using it both constructively and creatively. This tells you that the things and conditions you desire to become reality must first be created in thought.

Your code will explain and guide you through the process. It will equip you with a greater personality, a worthy purpose, and a new ability to enjoy life's beauties and wonders.

DISCUSSION QUESTIONS

- What is the contents of the Moscow Mathematical Papyrus?
- What is Pure Mathematics?\

'DOWN THE RABBIT HOLE'

'So Above, So Below'. There is nothing made that does not have, shape, and dimension. Everything in all things is traced back to numbers. The first cause of the creative idea or the last manifestation of matter. The aspects of numbers allow the past, present, as well as future, to be defined. Make no mistake, numbers are the ideal relationship within the universe. Numbers are the purest expression of truth because they determine the exact relationship between cause and effect.

The notion of numbers can sometimes be difficult to comprehend. It's important to understand the historical evolution of the representation of numbers for communication and manipulation; (the numbers of life, and the intrinsic structure of those numbers. The two perspectives synergistically inform each other and allow one's understanding to grow and evolve with the numbers themselves.

The womb is the physical Zero (0), a place where hue-mans begin life. The place where all that is known (and knowable) about the idea of life can be discovered. That discovery will include the knowledge that hue-mans cannot fully know everything about themselves because everything living is always changing.

The mathematical Zero is often associated with a lack of nothing, but the cultural meaning is powerful and paradoxical. Zero is the first number in the real world, the nothingness from which we begin counting all things real and imaginary. Zero is the starting point for counting up and the endpoint for countdowns. Zero is one of two numbers in the binary system of the virtual world. 1 is the number for ``ön"and 0 is the number for "off".

Zero (0) is the identity element in an additive group or the additive identity of a ring. It
is the embodiment of nothing. In geometry, the dimension of a point is 0. In Algebra, Limits and differentiation are important. The limits of certain expressions in (x) as (x) approaches zero (0) is INFINITY etc. The mathematical principle is that (x) or (y) may either approach (0) or infinity, but never get there. A bit like walking from one wall to another halving each step you take (you can never get to the other side)

Astronomically the zero (0) represents the circle which has 360°, which is made up of 120° knowledge + 120° wisdom + 120° understanding.

The ratio of the circumference of a circle to its diameter (3.142857143...) keeps on going 4ever without ever repeating. Even if you took the 4 off it would still be unmeasurable. This means that contained within this string of decimals is every single other number. Your birth date, the password to your computer, your

National Insurance Number, it is all in there, somewhere. And if you convert these decimals into letters, you will have every word that ever existed in every possible combination. The first syllable you spoke as a baby, the name of your latest girlfriend/boyfriend, your entire life story from beginning to end. All the world's infinite possibilities rest within this one simple circle. Now what you do with that information, what it is good for is entirely up to you.

The female womb. 00.00.0000

DISCUSSION QUESTIONS

- Do you blame your problems and failures on others?
- What responsibility (if any) do you own for not getting on with family members or siblings?

NUMBERS AND THEIR MYSTERIES

Welcome to the world of numbers. What is it that makes numbers such a fascinating topic? I believe the fascination that numbers have for us arises from their great significance as reasoning devices, as powerful and highly flexible mental tools. Here is a passage by the 19th/20th century mathematician Richard Dedekind that emphasises the role that this concept of numbers plays in our thinking: "Of all the devices the hue-man mind has created to make its life - that is, the task of reasoning - easier, there is none that has such a great effect and is so indivisibly connected to its innermost nature, as the concept of numbers. [...] Every thinking hue-man, even if he does not feel it clearly, is a numerical being [...]."

What is your definition of a number? Numbers are at once practical notions in our every? The distinction between numbers and numbers is subtle. Numbers at once are practical notions in our everyday world and abstract objects from our imagination. Before our Ancestors could write, they contemplated quantities. Historically, the study of numbers was a central component of one's education – one of the liberal arts. Many people incorrectly believe that mathematics is completely understood; most of the mathematics remains a mystery. Forward progress is extremely slow-moving and discoveries in mathematics are made by building on the work of others who came before. Some ancient civilisations recorded their work on material that has stood the test of time... Others employed materials that, over time disintegrated: thus, our knowledge is as fragmented as the ancient, broken tablets we try to understand. Despite what many believe numbers are very difficult to define.

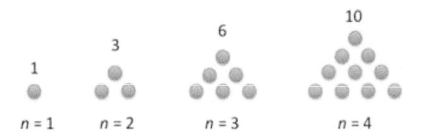

Briefly, all numbers come from zero/naught: 0, the cosmic egg in which all numbers are contained. The creator is also known as Alpha and Omega: 1 and 0, the first and the last. Together 1 and 0 form, the perfect number, and since it is supposedly perfect, it is the sacred number of the universe and is written as (1 or x) meaning "God in all"

Numbers symbolise all the good and bad that humans encounter in life. Each number is like a balance within the spirit of the creator. The sacred shapes of geometry that were looked at earlier holds the key to what is being discussed here. (*Based on the tree of life*)

1.   Will   ↔   Unwilling

2.   Wisdom   ↔   Foolishness

3.   Understanding   ↔   Ignorance

4.   Mercy   ↔   Inhumanity

5.	Leniency	↔	Severity
6.	Beauty	↔	Ugliness
7.	Victory	↔	Defeat
8.	Glory	↔	Disgrace
9.	Foundation	↔	Foundationless
10.	kingdom	↔	Subservient, surrender,

weakness

When we journey beyond the universe of numbers and delve into the more abstract world of infinity, we find that the ancestral method of counting numbers, understanding signs and symbols, can be understood and holds many surprising features.

The term Tetrarchy means four. (*revisit the chapter on Geometry Sacred Shapes*) There are four dots across the bottom, along each side, and one in the centre, 10 in total. When you add the first four numbers $1 + 2 + 3 + 4$, the total is 10. To many this is proof that all 10 powers of creation exist in the number 4. Hence the reason why the number 10 was the ideal number which represented the universe. The dots in the triangle are referred to (Yods) in Hebrew which means "The origin of all things". The first three Yods represent the threefold whitelight which is the Godhead, containing potentially all sound and colour, the unconscious universal mind - the creative principle of will, wisdom, and activity. The last seven Yods, or respectables of light, hold much meaning - seven visible planets, seven notes of the musical scale, and the seven primary colours, all of which are the creative forces which emanate from the primordial cause that created the universe

DISCUSSION QUESTIONS

- As you travel on your journey wondering 'why', you meet a man with seven wives; every wife has seven sacks, every sack has seven cats, every cat has seven kittens, kittens, cats, sacks, and wives. How many were travelling as you were wondering 'why'?
- What 3 things are the most important to you? Would you put those 3 things before achieving your goal?

THE SCIENCE OF NUMBERS

In the book; *Study Of Numbers by R.A. Schwaller de Lubicz*, states: *that the common function which determines past, present, and future decomposes into these three times beginning from the moment that the first One – the first, indivisible, purely qualitative, purely abstract cause distinguishes itself into the nine other numbers that thereafter will constantly accompany it. The first cause has potentially in it all future causes.*

What are numbers? Mathematical numbers are not discovered but generated or counted by adding monads. Any two monads constitute the mathematical number

(1) 'Monad', The first unity, the cause without a cause. Nothing to divide, nothing to share. The number one is purely qualitative, without quantity. As the first unity, it in certain expressions is seen as 'the absolute. The indivisible (1) is responsible for the first divisible number. Monad is the origin of all thoughts and contains all wisdom, for all numbers proceed from and are hidden in the Monad.

(2) 'Duad' in its abstract nature is (1) a concrete and divisible unity. The mystical nature of numbers suggests that the Creator is One because within that one finds the creative principle, a creative son, and a binding spirit that binds them all together... So, the number one is a creative one but manifested, giving you (2). Duad is the dividing line between spirit and matter. It represents all duality,

all opposite, all diversity. The hieratic secret of the Duad is the 'Tree of Knowledge of Good and Evil, the fruits of which can be beneficial or deadly.

(3)'Triad', highly revered by the ancestors. One or two lines could not represent a figure, but three lines form the triangle, the first figure. The union of the Monad and Duad produces the Triad. The common function which determines past, present, and future decomposes into these three times beginning from the moment that the first one – the first indivisible, purely qualitative, purely abstract cause – distinguishes itself into the nine other numbers that thereafter will constantly accompany it. The first cause has potentially in it all future causes. Hence it presents another state, simultaneity, that comprises past, present, and future in a single absolute. This is the fourth time.

By the coordination of these times, as well as by the diversity of the double nature of numbers, one obtains harmonies and dissonances, pure and mixed colours, and whole and fractional weights. This is the reason for cosmic harmony.

(4) 'Tetrad, harmony is manifested in the complementary arrangement of harmonies and dissonances. This mutual "complementation" of two natures gives birth to new unities, which are then complex and whose base is abstract Unity. These new units will be the origin of manifested numbers and their quantitative nature. In this way, values develop. Everything that exists has to

start with (1) and go through three successive stages to reach form in 4: idea, a seed planted, growth, mature product.

There are also four liberal arts: geometry, mathematics, music and astronomy, all of which are important in understanding other sciences.

(5) 'Pentad', harmony can only reign in the world if multiplicity disengages itself from manifested, hence divisible, Unity. This function is the same as that by which multiplicity disengages itself from the abstract One, but the act is now complicated by the fact of the preceding creation. What is created in the abstract becomes the first procreation in the formative idea. This idea again procreates a second time, and then the concrete world is manifested, because only in it can what is procreated procreate in its turn. The (5) represents equilibrium. The ancestors believe that the row of numbers 1-9 in sequence formed a beam of balance, and man is perfectly balanced at the centre. The Pentad was often called "Justice" for it was the instrument keeping balance between the celestial and bestial.

(6) 'Hexad' is a perfect number because it is the only number from 1-10 that is completely equal in its divisions, and it produces a hexagon when six lines are circularly drawn and adjoined. The 6 is associated with symmetrical and well-formed bodies, graceful curves and rounded figures where symmetry and balance are evident.

(7) 'Heptad', the vehicle of life" as it contains body and soul (4 being matter and 3 being spirit). It has also been calculated that the tones of

the planets according to their distance from each other, reasoning that their movement creates a vibration, which turns mathematical proportion into enlightenment.

(8) 'Ogdoad', the first cube of energy having eight angles. Considered the only ëvenly even"number between 1 and 10, (7 + 1, 6 + 2, 5 + 3) leaving no remainder. The 8 symbolises divine and material power, "As Above So Below".

(9) Ennead all numbers are contained within the number 9. All numbers following, when added together to the last digit, cannot produce a number higher than 9 as its root. Regardless of how much we learn, we must always return to our source in 10, forming the never-ending circle of existence. More often we experience an initiation in the form of a dream, which is a true experience in the higher realms of the astral world. The matter was represented by the number 9, or 3 x 3. It was noted that all material was composed of three elements: Water, Earth, and Fire and that those three elements each contained a little of each. Therefore 3 x 3 becomes a symbol of all body formation of matter.

(Morals and Dogma, 636).

(10) 'Decad' comes from the root word dechomai, meaning, "to receive". To the Ancestors, 10 was "the great number" symbolizing perfection: 1 being the spirit, embodied in nature which is 0.

(Moral and Dogma, 634).

DISCUSSION QUESTIONS

- Can you experience fulfilment solely by yourself, or do you require others?
- Is finding self-fulfilment secondary to other things in your life?

CONNECTED COMPONENTS

If asked today what "analysis" means, most people would immediately think of breaking something down into components to display its logical structure. Analysis has always relied on contrast with other approaches to help clarify its nature.

The logical foundation of analytic and synthetics as it is often taught is unclear. Analytic philosophy started in the late 1940s here in the UK and the US. It's a new radical way to approach philosophy. It emphasizes the clarity of thought under language, whether it makes sense or not

1. A code is perfect or imperfect (numbers, values, and relationships)

2. A soul corresponds with a code (disengagement of numbers)

3. The code is the quality of the first part of the soul, followed by the opposite quality of the second part of the soul (complementary arrangement of numbers)

4. The first part of the soul is the substance the first part of the code refers to (development of values)

5.   The second part of the soul is the opposite quality of the quality found in the second part of the code (establishment of cosmic harmony)

6.   The third part of the soul is the result of the conjunction of the first and second parts of the soul (qualitative relation)

7.   The fourth part of the soul clarifies how it is the opposite of the first part of the soul (additive inverse) e.g. -7(number) $+$ 7(additive inverse) $= 0$

DISCUSSION QUESTIONS

- Do you prefer to learn from others or from your mistakes? Why?
- Do you listen more than you speak?
- Do you allow your ego to get in the way of learning from someone you don't respect?

FORMATION MODE (This back-end tool will set the threshold for measure to be value)

- Set of generic numbers with the ability to find their completion.

- Hue-man code (ruling number) is defined by the process of accumulation and abstraction.

- Code is momentarily equal to that which gives birth to it.

- Active cause and passive cause are defined.

- Understanding the cause of variations in tendencies.

- 2, 4, 6, 8 (harmonic) not creative by themselves, feminine.

- 3, 5, 7, 9 (de-harmonic) creative and masculine.

- 1, is an even and odd number which makes it (father and mother of all numbers).

- 0, (most powerful symbol) all knowledge, all powers.

- Hexagon, polygon, triangle, pentagon, square, parallelogram (addition of triangular and square figures) relates to forms, numbers, and patterns.

- Forms (expressing numbers using words).

DECIMAL NUMBER SYSTEM (DNS)

Counting as we have been taught since childhood is based on the decimal number system. Decimal means base 10 (the prefix dec). In any number system, given the base (often referred to as radix), the number of digits that can be used to count is fixed. For example, in the base 10 number system, the digits that can be used to count are 0, 1, 2, 3, 4, 5, 6, 7, 8, 9.

Consider the number 1234. It can be represented as: $1 \times 10^3 + 2 \times 10^2 + 3 \times 10^1 + 4 \times 10^0$

(1) is in the thousand columns, (2) is in the hundred columns, (3) is in the tens columns, (4) is in the unit column.

Binary Number System (BNS)

Binary means base 2 (the prefix bi). The digits in the decimal number system that can be used to count in this number system are 0 and 1. The 0, 1 used in the binary system are called binary digits (bits)

The bit is the smallest piece of information that can be stored in a computer. It can have one of two values 0 or 1. Think of it a bit like a switch that can be either on or off.

Consider the binary number 1101. It can be represented as: $1 \times 2^3 + 1 \times 2^2 + 0 \times 2^1 + 1 \times 2^0$

To represent larger numbers, we must group a series of bits. Two of these groupings are very important:

Nibble – a group of four bits, Bytes – a group of eight bits

DISCUSSION QUESTIONS

- What is your definition of how the universe came to be?
- Do you believe we are alone in the universe? Why?
- What is the purpose of a cosmologist?

Converting from Decimal to Binary to Hexadecimal

Decimal	Binary	Hexadecimal
0	0000	0
1	0001	1
2	0010	2
3	0011	3
4	0100	4
5	0101	5
6	0110	6
7	0111	7
8	1000	8
9	1001	9
10	1010	A

11	1011	B
12	1100	C
13	1101	D
14	1110	E
15	1111	F
16	10000	10

BINARY 2 HEXADECIMAL

Convert the following binary into hexadecimal numbers: (00101111)

Referring to the table above: $0010 = 2$ $\quad$ $1111 = F$ $\quad =$
$(00101111)_2 = (2F)_{16}$

While this system has been applied in ancient Africa, the binary system has become the language of electronics and computers in the modern world. This is the most efficient system to detect an electrical signal: off (0) and on (1) state... It is also the basis of binary code used to compose data in computer-based machines. The text you are currently reading right now consists of binary numbers.

It's important to note; this is a positional system; therefore, every digit in a binary number is raised to the powers of 2, starting from the right-most with 2^0.

DISCUSSION QUESTIONS

- What is binary and what is its purpose?
- Non-Binary Sex: What is that?

DECIMAL 2 BINARY

Converting from decimal to binary can be a little tedious. We want to take the number and continuously divide it by 2, rounding down for decimals, and listing the numbers out. Each even number we represent with a 0 and each odd number we represent with 1.

That's a lot of words. Maybe an example will make things clearer. Let's convert 42_{10} (the little (10) means base-10) to base-2. Start by dividing 42 by 2 until we get down to a 1.

START

42

$\downarrow$ ÷2

21 ⟍ ÷2

10 ←—— round down —— 10.5

$\downarrow$ ÷2

5 ⟍ ÷2

2 ←—— round down —— 2.5

$\downarrow$ ÷2

1

END

Looking from the bottom number up, we have the numbers:

125102142.

The final step is to put a 1 under the odd numbers and a 0 under the even.

125102142101010 So: 42_{10} = 1010102.

DIRECTLY PROPORTIONAL

Before a tree can bear fruit, it must grow in strength and maturity. So be it with hue-man life. Achieving your primary purpose will strengthen your resolve...

When we first start in life, things just seem to happen to us randomly. As we mature, we notice patterns repeating themselves, and that there may just be some order to life. Many of us go through life dealing with one crisis after another, asking ourselves, is there a deeper meaning to all this madness? Is it possible someone, somewhere can explain what the hell is going on in this chaotic life of mine?

Just know that there is indeed coded information, spiritually designed to manage each moment of your life. Once you have access, your life seems to make total sense.

As we seek to connect with our higher self (hue-man code) we will begin to remove the layers of fakery you have clothed yourself in (the impression you want the world to see). Removing these layers is like a caterpillar shedding its skin. Caterpillars are primed to become butterflies from birth. Even in the smallest caterpillar, just hatched from the minuscule egg, bundles of cells are already primed, destined to become adult features such as antennae, wings, legs, and genitalia. The same applies to us as hue-mans. We have been primed; our code holds all the information we need to succeed in life.

You are ENDOWED at birth with your code. These numbers tell you the lessons to be learned during your life and the spiritual growth and development which you can attain. Your b-code accesses your life journey, it exposes your essence, your mystical connections are revealed, as well as your path of development. Your b-code is determined by the numbers in your earth date.

To arrive at the numerical vibration, each number has a mathematical and universal meaning which can be converted to letters in the alphabet which are valued as follows. A is 1; B is 2; C is 3; and so on to Z, which is 26. To work with the value of the letters beyond I, which is number 9, we reduce the value to a single digit. For example, L is number 12. We reduce the 12 by adding the first and second numbers together.

Example: 23rd May 1983 = 2 + 3 + 5 + 2+ 9 + 8 + 3 = 32, therefore 3 + 2 = 5. The ruling vibration of this date is the number (5). Five is the middle number (1-9), the centre as we would say, is the sum of two feminine numbers, it also relates to the (5) senses of touch, taste, sight, smell, and hearing, the path of Venus in its orbit (change, freedom, variety). The metaphysical meaning of numbers, their value, and their relationship to other numbers (unity and multiplicity with a fixed quantity of degree and variation), as well as its accidental aspect and its abstract life, are all relevant components.

The true nature of this science is not a secret. It may seem confusing at the 1st, 2nd, or even the 3rd stage, but it only seems confusing to those who are willing to learn.

The nature of numbers has two common functions: succession, by which the past, the present and simultaneity, as well as the future is defined.

Creation of numbers R. A. Lubicz

DISCUSSION QUESTIONS

- Is there something rather than nothing?
- How does sleep affect illnesses such as Diabetes and Obesity?
- In what way does meditation change sleep?

METAPHYSICAL NUMBERS

As previously mentioned, numbers assume a more profound significance. They represent aspects of what it is to be human. To truly understand this number science, we must first know the essential metaphysical meanings of the arcane meanings taught over 4,000 years ago by our ancestors.

ZERO is a symbol/number. Story has it that the zero supposedly began when King Shulgi implemented 'positional notation' in his mathematical state. The king'' positional notation was in base 60, not base 10. The middle eastern kingdoms who eventually became Babylonia are the ones responsible for our 360 degrees in a circle, 60 minutes in a degree, 60 seconds in a minute. The babylonian base-60 notation is similar to the base-10 10 system used.

ZERO (0) is present in many birth dates and has an important symbolic significance. Philosophically and mathematically, it represents nothing (as the numerator) and everything (as the denominator), the two infinite ends of the finite, neither of which is physically attainable. Thus, it is a mystical symbol, indicative of the degree of spiritual mysticism inherent (but rarely developed) in the individual. Anyone who has one or more zeros in their birth date has an inherent spirituality that they should recognise, for it has the potential to assist them in understanding many of the deeper aspects of life (such as life's purpose, the power of thought and the process of reincarnation).

ONE (Monad) is the first physical number. As the only absolute number, it is the symbol of divine expression. It is the key to verbal self-expression and the expression of the ego as a microcosm of the divine (the macrocosm), the key to communication skills. This is the point when the creator makes himself known to the world. The beginning of all things lies motionless within Monad, the origin of all thoughts and contains all wisdom for all numbers proceed from and are hidden in the Monad.

TWO (Dyad) is the first spiritual (feeling) number. It represents the duality of humans and symbolises the gateway to our sensitivities, as well as our need to be part of a pair. This is the number of intuitions that represents the beginning of the knowledge of good and evil, the dividing line between spirit and matter. It represents all duality, all opposites, all diversity. Similar to the tree of good and evil, the fruit which can be beneficial or deadly

THREE (Triad) is the first mind (thinking) number. Following the primary verbal (1) and intuitive (2) expressions comes the mental. It is the gateway to the conscious mind and rational understanding, the focus of left-brain activity, the key to memory. The number 3 is symbolised by the triangle, representing the connection of mind, soul and body. This is the number that gives support to a physical thing, making the triangle so powerful. When understanding aligns with will and wisdom it forms a triangle of power.

FOUR (Tetrad) is the number at the centre of the physical (doing) plane, the key to orderliness, practicality and organising. It is symbolised by the square, the basis of all practical construction. Everything starts with 1 and goes through three successive stages to reach form in 4: idea, seed planted, growth, matter brought into being.

FIVE (Pentad) is the centre of the soul (feeling) plane and the very centre of the total birth chart. It is the spiritual number representing love and freedom of expression. 5 also represents equilibrium as it is exactly in the middle from 1 through to 10. it also denotes one who has limited knowledge of that which is higher than itself. The pentagram is an emblem, the five-pointed star which is known as the symbol of safety, that middle ground of balance because of the dual influence of the 5. Taking this a little step further the number 5 is also the number of man because man has five senses and five distinct extremities: two arms, two legs, and a head that directs the other four. Like nature, 5 reproduces itself by its own seed, because when it is multiplied by itself it returns to itself by producing its own number, showing up as part of the total. Example; $5 \times 5 = 25$, $5 \times 15 = 75$, $5 \times 25 = 125$, etc. In the law of opposites, the 5 is masculine and feminine, and for us to be well balanced, we must have a small amount of the opposite force. The male must have some receptivity to soften his nature, and the female must have some positive force to give her strength.

SIX (Hexad) is the centre of the mind (thinking) plane, where it represents creativity, the integration of the left and right lobes of the brain. It also represents the opposite of creativity – destruction. This is "negative" creativity expressed as worry, stress, anxiety and depression. The number six is known as a perfect number because it is the only number from one to 10 that is completely equal in its divisions $(1 + 2 + 3)$.

SEVEN (Heptad)is the symbol of the temple, the human body and its seven chakras or power centres. It is the teaching-learning number, the number of practical philosophical experiences. Such learning is usually acquired through sacrifice as the means of indelible instruction. The number seven is known as the symbol of the ensouled. The spiritual man is known to have seven senses, the five physical including sight, touch, smell, taste, and hearing, plus mental perception and spiritual understanding. Because the number 7 contains 3 and 4: 4 being matter and 3 being the spirit that activates it. The difference between the material and spiritual man is; material man is able to gain much through intellect, but until there is that inner illumination of the spiritual self, he cannot grow to his full potential.

EIGHT (Ogdoad) is the most active spiritual number, situated at the active end of the soul plane. It is the number of wisdom expressed intuitively through loving action. It brings independence into focus. The number 8 is like a double mirror that sees (understands) both worlds which represents good judgement. The symbol for infinity ∞ is also a pictorial symbol of the orbital movement of the planets and their regular and constant serpentine paths in the universe. The number 8, similar to 0, can be written over and over again without lifting the pen from the paper, which symbolises divine and material power

NINE (Ennead) is the three-fold number at the action end of the mental plane. As the mind in action, it represents ambition (the physical aspect), responsibility (the thinking aspect) and idealism (the spiritual aspect), and so combines the attributes of each of the previous numbers, known as "the horizon and the ocean" All materials are composed of three elements; water, earth, and fire, and those elements contain a little of each other. Therefore 3 x 3 becomes a symbol of all body formation of matter. The number 9 is also a finishing number, bringing to an end, because it takes nine months for a baby to be formed, and when complete there is birth. Hence 9 is perfecting the finishing for the new birth which is in 10.

Ten (Decad) meaning "to receive". It represents heaven, the origin of numbers, the container of all things. The number 10 symbolises perfection: 1 being the spirit, embodied in nature which is 0. Within the law of opposites, 10 is limited and unlimited, similar to 1. The 1 is found in every number and every number has proceeded from 0 and is contained within it. 1 being the masculine creative force and the 0 being the feminine uniting to form the Yod of creation. As time passed the Yod became a phallic symbol of the father, and the moon of the mother aspect of the Godhead. The moon is related to the mother and creation because the woman's reproductive system is on a monthly 28-day lunar cycle.

DISCUSSION QUESTION
- Does your body size affect your sleep??
- Can you solve problems by dreaming about them?

ASPECTS OF LIFE.

Basic Self, accessing the (5) physical senses (seeing, touching, tasting, and smelling), together with talking, laughing, and crying. Those who function from their basic aspect are ego motivated. Motivation at this level will be reactive once the physical activities have been mastered. Your basic self is vital to your overall balance. Once the basics are mastered it becomes a faithful servant. The formula for (ego) mentioned earlier in the book will help you in a way that your basic self is the slave of the ego, not its master. Thus, allowing the lessons of life to be readily recognised.

Conscious Self – translates spiritual awareness into physical consciousness. It interprets your thoughts, attitudes, and emotions such as joy, sadness and ability. This is the area of memory, creativity, and idealism. Logically speaking, when you decide to operate negatively (- number), the Conscious self (+ number) becomes unconscious self, reactive, stress-driven, deceitful, etc. Consciousness aligns itself with memory as it links past, present, and future *(code)*

DISCUSSION QUESTIONS
- Is sex good for your sleep?
- Does pregnancy alter the sleep of the female?
- What does marijuana do to your sleep?
- What does cocaine do to your sleep

SELF DISCOVERY

Hue-man beings are the only creatures who are endowed with divine light from the time of their creation. Those born with high IQ are gifted to grasp higher knowledge and wisdom thus adding to the benefit and advancement of the hue-man civilisation. As hue-mans, every era has evolved with individual and collective consciousness. Each hue-man is a gifted creature; his/her extreme good nature is a boon to our kind and all members of our society.

Good and evil tendencies reside in our nature which rises in our personality. Our evil tendencies can cause us to harm not only others but ourselves. This could be due to severe hurt caused to one's personality and ego being injured (trauma). For one's pride to be restored generally revenge kicks in while seeking self prestige or glorification.

Man and His Symbols, a book written by *Carl G. Jung*, the famous psychoanalyst and the Father of Analytical psychology; is an amazing piece of work with well over 400 illustrations explaining the relationship between man and symbols. The book opens up with the statement "Man uses the spoken or written word to express the meaning of what he wants to convey. His language is full of symbols, but he often employs signs and images that are not strictly descriptive. Some are abbreviations or strings of initials such as UN, UNICEF OR UNESCO, others are familiar trademarks, the name of patent medicines, badges or insignia. Although these are meaningless in themselves, they have acquired a recognisable meaning through common usage or deliberate intent. such things are not symbols. They are signs and they do more than denote the objects to which they are attached.

To discover yourself and to answer the question Who am I? one needs to have a thorough understanding of the symbolic language and its association with hue-man inner consciousness and his self. The ancestral man's symbols are deeply inherent in the hue-man psyche and the same occurs in each individual's conscious and unconscious level and plays an important role in the makeup of his personality. A person consciously or unconsciously identifies himself with the ancient symbols inherited by him with his desires, frustrations, aims and objectives in trying to find the meaning of life.

Man is endowed with many qualities both negative and positive and all his characteristics, behaviour, moods, eccentricities are all linked to thousands of symbols and signs created by The One.

Understanding yourself requires merging yourself so that you begin to feel yourself… you no longer seek peace, tranquillity, equilibrium, balance and harmony because you now understand the symbols and numbers that rule your life.

Being able to understand this concept well enough allows you to be able to foresee many phenomenons.

Numbers have high philosophical importance as well as a practical value, hence the mystery. If you are prepared to research and study the metaphysical aspects of numbers, the truth will be revealed and only then will you understand the mystery.

Numbers connect cause and effect. In Astronomy, numbers are a value unsuspected by the uninitiated. You should only attribute the correct virtues which are classifications of the poles and relationships that bind the effect with the cause...

Numbers allow you to specifically specify times, duration in relation to unity: day, year, month, etc. The initiated will know all the essential conditions necessary for hue-man development. Numbers are distinct vibrations. There is not a thing that exists that does not vibrate. Vibration is measurable, and to measure we must use numbers. Each number is a law to itself, which never deviates from the principle behind the law that governs it, it one being a symbol for a type of influence or energy. Therefore numbers can be applied to everything that has existed, and that number includes its qualities and characteristics, including its opposite, giving you a positive and negative.

Then this is the secret that makes Astronomical and Mathematical *code deciphering* work. Letters are symbols for sound, sound vibrates and creates form and has its traits. To know those rates of vibration, we need numbers.

DISCUSSION QUESTIONS

- How would your partner having an online relationship affect you?
- What is your definition of unfaithfulness?
- Would your relationships benefit if the man had two wives?

Judges in the United States, the United Kingdom, and Canada have ruled that it was necessary to see a person's face to detect deception. Witnesses may not wear the niqab-a type of face veil-when testifying, in part because they believe.

The permissibility of the niqab has also been called into question by the court dismissing a plaintiff's complaint when she refused to remove her veil to testify.

Similarly, in Canada, an alleged victim of childhood sexual assault was ordered to testify at a preliminary inquiry without her niqab.

(Muhammad v. Enterprise Rent-A-Car, 2006; R. v. N. S., 2010; The Queen v. D(r), 2013

Research has found no empirical evidence in the lie detection literature suggesting that a niqab should impair lie detection because it conceals portions of the wearer's face; rather, existing research suggests that the opposite could occur. Niqabs should minimise the amount of information that is available to observe and prevent them from basing their lie detection decision on misleading facial cues. (e.g., smiling; *DePaulo et al., 2003)*

The letters and numerical signs are of course the basic elements of all sciences. Each sign represents an absolute or essential idea. Please note that the form of each cypher and each letter has its mathematical reason and hieroglyphic significance. Ideas, inseparable from numbers, follow their movement by addition, multiplication, etc., and acquire their exactitude. *(The Book of Splendours, 136)*

HEX TRANSLATION

1-A	10-J	19-S	= 1	A,J,S
2-B	11-K	20-T	= 2	B,K,T
3-C	12-L	21-U	= 3	C,L,U
4-D	13-M	22-V	= 4	D,M,V
5-E	14-N	23-W	= 5	E,N,W
6-F	15-O	24-X	= 6	F,O,X
7-G	16-P	25-Y	= 7	G,P,Y
8-H	17-Q	26-Z	= 8	H,Q,Z
9-1	18-R		= 9	I,R

MELANIN:

M	13	4
E	5	5

L	12	3
A	1	1
N	14	5
I	9	9
N	14	5
TOTAL	*73*	*32 (Root Total)= 5 (Root Number)*

The full word total, 73, comes directly from the order of balance (equilibrium}.

The number 5 is also the number of men. Melanin allows hue-men to be balanced.

OUR CODE?

Within each person is a beautiful light waiting to shine forth, a magnificent being aching for expression. That is the inner self, our individuality, our essential uniqueness. But this is not what we generally present to the world. Instead, we have produced a "personality," a composite expression at the crux of which is our individuality (our inner self). The average person is often two people. That which is freely expressed is usually the image, while the real person, the unique individuality of our inner self, is all too frequently suppressed. The image is something of an emotional ghost we have cultivated to defend our sensitivities. But we sell ourselves far too short, for our image can never hold to the beauty and grandeur of our natural inner self. The acute sensitivity of the inner self is often mistaken for vulnerability, and as a consequence, we build up a psychological wall. We stifle it, refusing to give it air, exercise and expression. We begin to understand the inner self only when we start to understand who we are, where we have come from, our purpose in choosing this life and how to achieve that purpose. In varying ways, we are all searching, but generally, the search is for something external. We need to realise that the answers lie within, for as thinking, sensitive people, we need more answers to life than religion, politics or science have so far delivered. We need guidance, not promises; examples, not theories. And this is what I will deliver on the pages that follow.

The Science of Numbers, as originally taught by the ancestors, is about to be revealed.

Our Ruling Number is found by first adding each number in our 'earth-date together. We then add those numbers together until we get a single-digit number. For example, if we take the birth date January 3, 1960, and rewrite it numerically as 1/3/1960, we get 20 as a result when we add all the numbers together: $1 + 3 + 1 + 9 + 60 = 20$. This total is then reduced to a single-digit number by simply adding $2 + 0$, which of course is 2. So, the Ruling Number of a person born on January 3, 1960, is shown as $1/3/1960 = 20/2$. To clearly illustrate how each Ruling Number (11 in total) is obtained, the following birth dates have been used as examples:

MARCH 3 NUMBER OF 2	1940 : 3/03/1940	= 20/2	RULING
AUGUST 8 NUMBER OF 3	1940 : 8/08/1940	= 30/3	RULING
APRIL 4 NUMBER OF 4	1940 : 4/22/1940	= 22/4	RULING
SEPTEMBER 3 NUMBER OF 5	1940 : 9/09/1940	= 32/5	RULING
MAY 5 NUMBER OF 6	1940 : 5/05/1940	= 24/6	RULING
JANUARY 1 NUMBER OF 7	1940 : 1/01/1940	= 16/7	RULING
MAY 6 NUMBER OF 8	1940 : 5/06/1940	= 26/8	RULING
FEBRUARY 2 NUMBER OF 9	1940 : 2/02/1940	= 18/9	RULING

| JULY 7 | 1940 : 7/07/1940 | = 28/10 | RULING |

NUMBER OF 10

| MAY 5 | 1940 : 5/19/1940 | = 29/11 | RULING |

NUMBER OF 11

| MAY 3 | 1940 : 5/03/1940 | = 22/4 | RULING |

NUMBER OF 22//4

Numbers 11 and 22, are considered as master numbers, which require the individual to understand the *Sacred Code* behind both 2 or 4 to gain a fuller understanding.

There is so much information about your true inner nature, as well as your overall purpose in life which you can look into when it comes to your *Code*.

ANCESTRAL TRANSMISSION OF COMPLEX TRAITS

Layered Representation of Genealogies

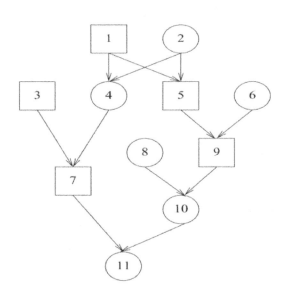

Ancestors reached 3 generations ago are parent and child. Consider individuals 1, 5 and 11. There are two paths from 1 to 11, namely path (1, 4, 7, 11) on the left-hand side of the genealogical graph and path (1, 5, 9, 10, 11) on the right-hand side. Hence both individuals 1 and 5 can be reached 3 generations ago from 11, and 5 is the child of 1. Males are represented by squares, females by circles.

Ancestral Transmission Benoit Deslauriers 2004

DISCUSSION QUESTIONS

- When you think about the lifestyle that you would most like to have, who do you feel most embodies it?
- Is there anyone you would not like to see succeed?

Can you picture people fighting to a love song? A person can be healed by the soothing sounds of his/her own keynote code. There are many healthy and unhealthy vibrations, and we take them in the same way we consume food. Our bodies find it difficult to adjust to the different types of food many of us consume on a daily basis.

This current system governed by prime numbers creates "Chaos", therefore our actions are unpredictable. We therefore need to become "Chaos" agents changing the future in an unpredictable manner. Our purpose is to make sure that the system is in "Chaos" to make it live.

THE SCIENCE BEHIND YOU

Your code is a master key to unlocking your meta-mathematical identity. It is an accurate code that reveals attributes of a higher dimensional expression of who you are, and what your vocation and blessings are to share with others. Your code is an affirmation that vibrates which you are supposed to feel, rather than relate to. If you continue to be curious your code's frequency will vibrate within you!!

This decoding is by no means a typical personality trait or name game. The purpose of this decoding is to guide you into your rightful position. Once you decode your code, you may feel awkward at first but as long as you are prepared to open up and embrace the vibrations your code sends you the meanings will reveal itself to you the more you interact. As you move forward the energy from your code will align you to where you are supposed to be.

(2) Duad Feminine

Very compassionate, very diligent and reliable. Ability to be good peace-makers and excellent reforming skills. You exhibit a noble and selfless acumen. You are also able to merge your ego with others when necessary. You are very sensitive and unassuming, you don't like to hog the limelight and are much more comfortable being in the supportive role. Your self confidence is not as high as other ruling numbers which makes you far less assertive. You are generally attracted to leaders/producers. Moving forward, for you to develop your potential you must be personally involved. If you allow materialism or a false sense of ego to take over you will become very frustrated as it is only an act which is not sustainable. You often attempt to use logical reasoning to justify behaviour which is not acceptable. You also have the tendency to allow your intuition to cloud your judgement. Your most suitable vocations: Singer (more comfortable in a group), personal assistant, working in a charitable education capacity, social worker. If limited by knowledge (process worker). In partnerships and groups, you will encounter the lessons you came to learn in this lifetime. Success is then very possible. You must have consideration for others and should bring people together for a common cause. Various professions are open to you as you learn to be adaptable to most things that need to be done. You could select a career in finance, music, medicine, religion or statistical analysis and research.

key elements: The positioning of your number is at the centre of your personal power, creativity, sexuality and finances. Issues surrounding physical health, and one - on - one relationship are at the core of your energy centre. Your main functions: procreation, assimilation of food, physical force, vitality and sexuality. In your relationship it's important to honour one another. Every relationship you develop is supposed to help you achieve a spiritual value. Over indulgence in food or sex will create confusion, create sexual difficulties, a sense of uselessness, jealousy, impotence, uterine and bladder problems. Once your resilience is low your wisdom is also low which makes you foolish/confused. It's really important as your number suggests that you focus on balance throughout your life...

Mystic virtues: Opposing dualities of dark and light, life and death, male and female, heaven and earth, yin and yang, tact and diplomacy...

(3) Triad Masculine

You have an active brain, general mental awareness and a lively sense of humour which can add to a successful social and working life. You are supercritical of your partner at home which can cause friction (putting it mildly). Mathematically you are a representation of the triangle which spiritually signifies; Father- Mother-Child, Soul-Spirit-Mind, Super-Conscious, Subconscious, Conscious. When two triangles are interlaced, geometry kicks in and captures the axiom, As above, so below. The upper triangle represents Ancestral spirit and the lower triangle represents worldly matters. Your primary purpose relates to your mental capabilities. Understanding your life purpose and development of your personality is significant to your thought process. Your ideal mode of expression is through thinking, planning, analysing, memorising and so forth. When you are not living constructively, you often assume an unpleasant air of superiority, which can create misunderstanding and lead to considerable happiness. The flip side of your mind state is capable of being less tolerant to those who are less mentally gifted. Which makes you very critical of the limitations of others. This is an ugly trait which can often expose itself in the home which can cause breakdowns in relationships. Developing a sense of sensitivity to the feelings of others is a must to aid your development. Taking responsibility for your own actions instead of trying to blame others when caught up in undesirable circumstances has to change. You have amazing powers or resilience, use it as an opportunity to grow. Within the home try to be more practical in your day-to-day affairs.. Your most suitable vocations; Business manager, system analyst, writer, art critic, accountancy, research scientist..

Key elements: Further the development of self-esteem and personality. Separate from your tribal identity, this is where you learn to draw on and maintain strong boundaries and a personal code of honour. Honour oneself, be mature and honourable in your relationship you have with yourself and accept responsibility for the person you have become. You have will, personal power, authority, energy, mastery of desire, self control, radiance, awakening, transformation, humour, laughter and immortality. Your qualities have to be managed otherwise you take on more that you can assimilate and utilise. Because of your traits you tend to put too much emphasis on power, and anger, which in-turn formulates fear and hate, which in-turn will cause you issues with your digestive system… Be mindful, there is a level of unworthiness that resides in you. Conscious communication is required.

Mystic virtues: combines the numbers one and two, which includes all life and experience. The three elements in man (body, reason, and spirit), three elements of faith (knowledge, assent, confidence). Self expression, communication

(4) Tetrad Feminine

You are systematic, reliable and trustworthy. Your accuracy, practical ability, and attention to detail is second to none... You are hardworking who enjoy seeing the results of your labour. Where intellectual or spiritual matters are concerned you are often more impatient. Your ruling number suggests that you are far more deeper than material things, even though one of your major emphasis aligns with the physical. Truth must come to you and not vice versa. This can only happen if your heart and mind are simple, clear and combined with love. You will never find the truth if your heart is filled with the things of the mind. You have an amazing gift which allows you to bring the truth into being. Once you are able to strip the mind of material things and cease to create, the truth will come to you without invitation. You are very much consumed in your own work causing you to unconsciously neglect the balance in your life, especially where the home, relationships and family life are concerned. If your emotional balance becomes weak you can easily lose heart due to frustrated lack of ambition, which often manifests into nerve problems and stress induced illness. Your materialist attitude is never too far away and if allowed to consume you will lead to emotional insecurity and serve unhappiness which will slow down your development and life purpose. Relaxation, mental application, and instinctive mind expanding are ways you can enhance your development. Meditation is the name of the game for you, an absolute must. It will allow you to focus more on memory retention. It's vital you strive for balance in your affairs, applying it especially to the part of the mind that deals with; creative and idealistic ideas, your spirituality, wisdom, instinctiveness and your love faculties. Your most suitable vocations;

skilled tradesperson, economist, teacher of art, sports & fitness, magazine author, manager. You are the number one doer and are very capable with your hands...

Key elements: You currently have a lack of trust in the flow of things. Share of self with others, e.g. children; trust more in all aspects of life. You have the capability of determining your own health, strength, and balance. Within you resides divine unconditional love, forgiveness, compassion, overstanding, balance, group consciousness, oneness with life, acceptance, peace, openness, harmony, contentment. On the flip side, repression of love, emotional instability, and out of balance, which in-turn can cause heart and circulation problems.

Mystic virtues: (prudence, tempemperance, fortitude, justice). Limitation, restrictions, hard work.

(5) Pentad Masculine

You are both temperamental and excitable. Freedom, change and adventure are what you are all about... You seem to be generally involved in many superficial interactions with others. You are fluent in communication, with little information about a lot of things, and a desire to travel all over to communicate. You also have irresistible magnetism to the opposite sex...

You will generally decide on a course of action and commit to it. You are also very connected to your emotions and your moral nature. Just as nature is free you are constantly striving to be just as free. Due to your emotions you carry around deep feelings which are best expressed in your artistic flair which will allow you to gain immeasurable pleasure in being free to express yourself. You are generally good natured with an emphasis on enjoying life and helping others to do so as well. Due to your strong desire for freedom you will(if the situation warranted) take on certain employment in illegal activities (cash-in-hand) to avoid being confined to an orthodox job. You hate having to answer to a boss and will take on another route such as claiming benefits (if warranted) just to be free. You get very nervous and become uncertain when confined to the 9 to 5 work-world which can be a precursor to stress and depression. You also make poor business people. Your number suggests that you are living in the past of care-free innocents but I'm sure you can appreciate that living in history is certainly not a precursor for future development. When feeling constricted it's important to learn lessons from that moment allowing you to move forward. It is important to increase your attention to detail allowing you to embrace a wider perspective of life. Opportunities for suitable travel should be grabbed with both hands allowing you to develop your powers of observation which in-turn will develop your wisdom. Regardless of how you represent yourself to the world you are very love-motivated, allowing you to genuinely respond and give it in return. Most suitable vocations; acting profession (in front or behind the cameras), politician, sales person, social worker, entrepreneur, designer, inventor, social- worker..

As mentioned above your nature is generally; loving, free, moody, artistic and adventurous. Bouncing between the different states when either allowed to be free or when feeling suppressed...

Key elements: You are currently consumed by the fear of speaking the truth, and the misuse of the power of your voice. This is currently at the centre of your struggle with choice and the ability to release your will to divine guidance.

It's essence is faith itself, faith in your fears or faith in the creator. Speaking your truth grounds the energy in and makes it tangible. To be the free spirit you crave, to surrender your personal will to the Divine Will, Your every choice, thought and feeling has biological, environmental, social, personal and global consequences, motivated by personal will. Freeing that free spirit in the correct manner will give you trust in the divine power which will give you what you have been craving for as well as the richest power. Power of the spoken word, true communication, creative expression in speech, writing, the arts, integration, peace, truth, knowledge, wisdom, loyalty, honesty, reliability, greatness and kindness. The flip side (similar to a coin with two sides): communication problems, knowledge used unwisely, ignorance, lack of confidence, depression, which in-turn can cause thyroid problems. Accepting yourself as a pioneer is as good a place as any to start from...

Mystic virtues: Your number is the sum of (2), a feminine number, and (3), a masculine number. Associated to the five senses: touch, taste, sight, smell, hearing. The number five also represents the number of zones in the world. Your focus must be; Change, freedom, variety

(6) Hexad Feminine

Your creativity looks for every opportunity to express itself in all areas of your life. Your home life is ultimately your number one place. It occupies a lot of your time and effort and is only superseded by your love for those who live within the home. Your potential for superior creativity is there for all to see when living positively. You have a tendency to become an incessant warrior when living negatively (it's all about that mathematical balance). You have the ability to perceive and create pure brilliance but your numbers suggest that any success achieved will not be lasting due to your tendency to self-destruct. In saying that you are capable of capturing the world stage of fame if you are focused and set your mind on it. As one of the people whose hindrance is to constantly worry, you have to be mindful of not getting caught up in a web of stress. It's important to master the arena that your creativity will take you otherwise you will let the situation control you. You will excel in positions where you are allowed to be creative, and trusted. If your creativity is confined to the home unhealthy anxieties can creep in and over-take you and possessiveness becomes the order of the day. which in-turn can add fear and anxiety to your worrying disposition restricting your personal growth. You can generally tell when you are in this state as you adopt the air of problem seekers and are constantly complaining. Your development and creativity requires a positive outlook especially where you have physical limitations. Your tendency to over worry can become very chronic bringing with it a sad and lonely outcome, totally conflicting with your creative nature. Your loving concerns should never remove your creative freedom of expression. Your desire for peace can also be construed as a sign of weakness. Developing firmness aligned with wisdom will guard you against thoughtless individuals who want to impose on your creativity, and it will also improve your happiness… Your vocations relate to working in the performing art world (singing, acting or both) as you often have the tendency to over dramatise your current situation. You have the ability to do very well in the humanitarian industry. If you decided to go down the route of being a healer of some capacity you wouldn't get lost.

Key elements: you lack focus, which is blocking your creativity, making you rigid and angry. Creative adventures; review and prioritise your goals, stay focused, complete them in manageable steps of success, harness the frustration. Your number suggests that you are at the centre of intuition, intellect and reasoning (known to some as the third eye). It's important to note your mental ability and your psychological will, when accessing your own beliefs and attitudes. Truth is your fuel, seek it continually. Search for the difference between truth and illusion, the two forces are present at every moment. Trust what you cannot see far more than what you can see. Soul realisation, intuition, insight, imagination, concentration, peace of mind and wisdom, devotion and perception beyond duality are the tools given to you to use. The flip side: your lack of concentration, fear cynicism will cause tension, headaches, eye problems, bad dreams..,

Mystic virtues: The number six is said to represent balance, love, health, love, and luck. In sacred geometry; six equally - sided circles can fit perfectly around a seventh of equal size. Home, responsibility, humanitarianism.

(7) Heptad Masculine

Are found amongst the most active individuals in life. Your numbers suggest you suffer rather sad lives, especially if you don't take heed from previous experiences. You gain your experience from life's lessons and the mistakes you make. You will sacrifice so much just to learn so that you can teach and share your wisdom more than any others. Any major development or steps forward that other numbers decide to take will have the soul incarnation of the ruling number 7. These individuals have a unique aspect with regards to their capacity for learning as it is almost limitless and generally comes from life experiences. Knowledge acquired in this capacity qualifies them as the number one teachers. Their personal experiences, equips them with a deep philosophy of life. You will not tolerate more than minimal direction from others, as you are hungry to learn via personal involvement which demands a certain level of sacrifice, which in-turn affects any or all of the following; health, relationship and finance. You are very good disciplinarians but do not take kindly to receiving discipline from others as you find it difficult to deal with.. You have the capability of being the most active in life compared to all the other ruling numbers. Many individuals who are ruling 7s often lead sad lives especially if they do not heed from previous experiences which can cause very harsh sacrifices. You also have a natural resilience that gives you self confidence which allows you to deal with life issues more stoically than others realise. You also have a certain arrogance about you in refusing to accept advice, which comes across as, you like to teach but you don't like to be taught. This attitude can cause you to lose out as you don't'' allow yourself to learn from others, but in-turn you want others to follow your advice. Unless wisdom prevails your domestic and business life will be far from happy. Your emphasis on gathering, retaining and sharing knowledge seems to stem from the fact that ruling 7'' are generally, not only slow learners, they also need to experience almost everything for themselves. Most suitable vocations; within the judicial or legal industry, surgeon, carpenter, butcher, lecturer, scientist, philosopher. It's really important that you are left to learn at your own pace..

Key elements: many of you are currently in dreamland, living with indecision. Open the heart, heal the heart, live from the heart and control hiding... You need to live in the moment, achieve personal relationships with the most high. You also need to remove all physical, psychological and emotional illusions from your life. To do this you need to let go of the past, do not anticipate the future and live in the present of the divine. You have the ability to unify the higher self with the hue-man personality, and you are also able to manage perception beyond space and time

Mystic virtues: represents the union of divinity (3) and Gaia (4). The four phases of the moon lasts for seven days and there are seven days in the week. The seven deadly sins are gluttony, sloth, lust, vanity, anger, envy, and avarice...their counterparts are the 3 theological and 4 cardinal virtues. Analysis, wisdom, spirituality.

(8) Ogdoad Feminine

You are capable of pushing others to success. You are capable of leading by example and very ambitious. You need to learn how to handle; power, authority and money. This relates to your difficulty in self-expression. You have a strong air of independence, you are also commercially oriented as well as deeply concerned for the sick and helpless. Guidance is required especially with handling children... as you are either overindulgent or exceptionally strict. Your number suggests that you are very extreme. you have the potential for great creativity when living positively. Independence is very important to you. You are very complex combined with wisdom and character, wisdom being very important to you. Showing appreciation is something you find difficult to express consistently (a vital component in a successful relationship). Personal security is also very high on your essential list. You seem very inconsistent when it comes to being compassionate and sympathetic to the needs of others. You are not keen on having others depend on you as you tend to become impatient with those people, as you feel it will hamper your progress. You have amazing potential to become super successful as long as you don't allow emotional misunderstandings to get in the way of your decision making. You tend to develop a deep sense of resentment if others infringe on your plans. You need a great deal of guidance but as you mature you will realise how happier you become when allowing your loving feeling to flow more naturally. Effort must be made to overcome this unsociable, cold manner especially towards loved ones once you become aware. Your most suitable vocations; executive, finance, banking, stock-broker, aircraft captain, nurse, vet.. Because you are the masters at masking their natural feelings for a long period of time (in some cases a life-time), professional acting is another vocation that you would excel in..

Key elements: you are currently; undergrounded, you are avoiding connections and there are also elements of unclear boundaries. Look after the body, and enjoy earthly life.

Mystic virtues: Infinity. The first cubic cubic number (2 x 2 x 2). Considered a perfect number. At eight months old a child has milk teeth and at eight years old they lose them. Materialism, money, power.

(9) Ennead Masculine

You should be the universal lover of humanity, patient, kind and understanding. You must show others the way as the wisdom you have access to is difficult for many others to access. Ambition, responsibility and idealism are your progressive growth qualities, with a heavy emphasis on personal responsibility. Your prime motivation is to put people before commodities. You are far more suited to art and humanitarianism rather than to commercial pursuits. You are an idealist at art even though in reality it is not always workable. You are very ambitious with an emphasis on personal responsibility. Honesty is important as well as natural to you which is why you assume others to be so inclined. If you are unable to adopt your ideals you seek to impress others with negativity kicks in. An indication of the negativity you find yourself in is when you become a hypocrite. Your ambitions can either destroy or dominate the integrity of your ideals which will eventually feed your ego, which is far from attractive. You then become abrupt in mannerism, your attitude becomes disruptive, which individuals in your life will find difficult to tolerate, especially if you become materially motivated. Numerology underpinned by mathematics can help you to realise your limitations and help you to understand others. Development of your wisdom and intuition requires patients and persistence which you will need to develop. You need to loosen up much more as you are viewed as overly serious. Indulging more in laughter and humour is one of the components required to give you a portion of the balance you need. Suitable vocations; administrator in an educational institute, or research facility, crime solving, healer, counsellor, acting or arts. Your trait suggests that you are extremely honest, ambitious, serious about life and you have difficulty saving money...

Key elements: you have a resistance to power, you have a victim consciousness, and there are also no limits to your boundaries. You need to surrender to your spirituality in every moment, which will allow you to stay grounded.

Mystic virtues: Considered a sacred number. Three multiplied by itself to give eternity, completion and fulfilment. The fruits of the holy spirit (love, joy, peace, endurance, gentleness, patience, meekness, faith, temperance, goodness), mystery, 3 x 3: the triple trinity. Humanitarianism

(10) Decad Feminine

You are physical doers that endow a power of flexibility and adaptability that produces a highly popular personality. Unconsciously you adopt an air of debonair and self-assurance reflected in your confidence. There is no greater range of expressions than that found in you. They vary from being the most likeable, (living positively) to being lost (floundering, insecure) this is when negativity takes over. You have the potential for brilliant success or you can languish in mediocrity. You are the number 1" with regard to adaptability and adjustment. These traits are key when it comes to assisting others to the changes of life. Your natural fearlessness potentially leads you into ventures others never consider or dream of. If one wants to enjoy the light-hearted pleasures of life, look no further than you. When you are emotionally hampered, without realising it you become despondent, which usually causes frustration which manifests itself by you becoming irritable or short-tempered. Your optimism knows no boundaries. Expressing the powerful ego (1) combined with infinite spiritual depth (0). Ego = 1/knowledge. Your confidence can often create disharmony unintentionally amongst those who find your self confidence too dominating. You have a tendency to get lost in conformity and find it difficult to accept mediocrity as the norm. Balance and awareness of your surrounding world needs to be considered more. especially in areas such as your attitude, compassion and reverence for life. Discriminating between important and nonsense in your life is vital as you often have the tendency to waste valuable time on worthless pursuits. Most suitable vocations; sports, entertainment, interior design, salesperson, politicians, business executive, architects, real estate agent.

Key elements: there is a denial of spirituality which can cause a misuse of power. Service to others and your spirituality is your key…

Mystic virtues: the foundation of most counting systems including the decimal system. Perfection and completion, order and the lost tribes of Israel. ($3 \times 3 + 1$).

DISCUSSION QUESTION

- What tool does a conductor use to conduct an orchestra?
- How are you going to utilise your code?

(11) Eleven Masculine

If you live positively and utilise the exceptional spiritual powers you can be very uncompromising and have a high level of morality and ethics and be profoundly reliable. On the flip side, your life can appear to be difficult and colourless if you are not living positively, in tune with your strengths. You often reject assistance when in need, which suggests that you need to recognise the benefits from the assistance offered. You are one of the best people equipped to guide humanity into the age of awareness. You are often diverted from your higher purpose because of life's physical attractions. The material life is generally uninteresting unless you choose to operate outside of your code. When living naturally you are extremely dependable, honest and just, with a deep love for loved ones. If life is not running as you expect you tend to become bitter and spiteful, often indifferent in your attitude towards others and what they do. If you become or show signs of apathy it's an indication that you have become consumed with materialism, finding very little solace. It's very important for you to be able to express your spirituality practically, guided by intuition rather than being motivated by reward, recognition or favours. Temptation to disengage from your responsibilities and live a non virtuous life is also part of your trait that many submit to. It's important to guard yourself from others who find your generosity a sign of weakness by putting extra demands on your financial resources. Most suitable vocation; educator, social worker, spiritual leader, personal growth instructor, performing arts (as long as the role has values), designers, inventors.

Key elements: recognise your lack of structure, tendency to lose your way, life and death. It's important to discern and live according to your truth.

Cosmic virtues: The first master number, transition, conflict, martyrdom, excess (10 + 1), incontinence, sin.

The Earth's 'Great Year' has 12 Zodiac Ages

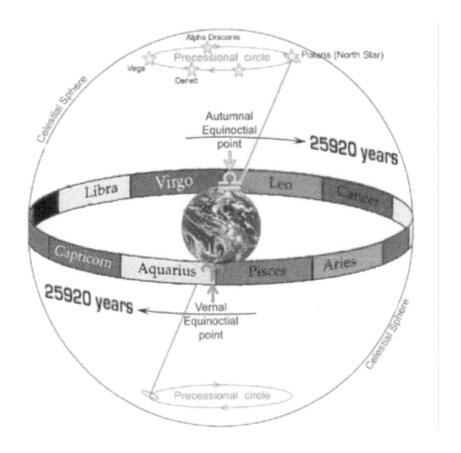

The "Great Year" is a 25,800 year cycle with 12 zodiac sub-cycles or ages of 2,150 years each. We are currently ending the age of Pisces and starting the age of Aquarius. The age of Pisces saw a rise in Christianity, and the age of Aquarius is defined by unified truth and brother-hood.

THE SUMMIT

I am an earnest seeker of the truth. Opinions and emotionalism
means very little to me, only truth. I have studied many religions
and have found positive elements in each one and the truths I have
come across I have embraced. But I have to admit I find the study of
numbers absolutely fascinating that I have not found anywhere
else. The study of numbers gives me: insight, answers, tolerance and
appreciation for other things. When you understand the meaning of
numbers you have the key to understanding.

When you use mathematical indicators you will find that motivation,
high achievement and understanding will join you. A mathematical
indication is anything that happens ahead of something else. In all
instances, the mathematical indicator comes ahead of the event in
which you are aligned (interested in).

To realise the answers to the many problems we face and to access our dreams, we must access the energy supply which is found when working through the numbers related to the tree of life. There are many who use meditation to connect with their inner circle, similar to renewing your mind.

You must have knowledge and know-how to interpret the meaning of what you observe and the numbers associated. It is no different than knowing that rain clouds precede rain, and falling leaves precedes winter.

It's also really important that we all listen!! Listening is the beginning of wisdom. True knowledge is an upliftment and heals every circumstance. The perfect law of the circle always metes out exact and right consequences, which is important to note..

We all have the ability to tap into our guidance number *(code)*. Actually, the full intent of the mysteries for all of us to know, is this one golden nugget of truth: we are all gods as God dwells in all hue-mans. Within the soul of each and every one of us there is that abiding light which is a ray from the Divine Being. Similar to how Yod appears in letters and numbers with its light of Wisdom from its source. All of our God-like qualities - love, compassion, understanding-emanate from this light.

CONCLUSION

None of us are born perfect, our purpose here is to evolve towards perfection. When we become aware of how this can be achieved, we realise that we need to stay here a long time to fulfil such a mission, rather than waste time in successive re-acquaintances with our physical bodies and this planet's unique spectrum of vibrations. This is where we have a choice – to grow a little each lifetime or to stay here and get it all done, making the very best of what we have.

Accessing your code gives you a flow of life, soul, spirit, and ancestors coming to and through you, allowing you to Co-create on earth at all levels in your life. It is your soul, spirit and code that is the source of your manifestation in your life, not your ego-mind. To Co-create requires working with the brilliant sparks of the ancestors awakening in you the great works. It's also important to search out like-minded ones so you can connect as a group. You will recognise them by the look in their eyes, that spark of the divine (knowing) looking back at you. The experience will be one of familiarity. You will fill a void in their life that they didn't know existed and they will fill a gap in your life you didn't know was still there. The connection will be strong at a code (soul) level.

The science of numbers is a wonderful guide to the constant creation of life, but remember as you travel 'down the rabbit hole', it is not the way the wind is blowing that determines our progress – over that we have no control; progress is only achieved by the way we set our sails.

Learn to trust the guidance of the universe but most of all learn to trust yourself. You will find that you are rarely wrong and with your understanding of your code and with the universe working with you, you are an unstoppable force.

Your journey of remembrance of who you truly are has begun. The truth about our imperfections is already known. With deeper knowledge, we can come to recognise the truth behind and within numbers.

In time you will begin to understand the cause that affects both your past, present and future. Don't believe everything you hear, read and watch. To puncture received ideas about culture, start thinking..

Your code holds the information of your life to help you along your journey. Continue to strive for what is true and when you find it create your balance...

Hotep!

WHAT IS THE PURPOSE OF THE NUMBER METHOD ADOPTED?

- It's used to give you the reader an insight into the tools I use to arrive at my conclusions and a means of you understanding what I think I know
- This' process was selected for its ability to rigorously test
- A multitude of truths and interesting facts are uncovered along the way
- The mathematical approach using geometry and astronomy in alignment
- Not diluted with information not originally ours (names)

ACKNOWLEDGEMENT

A book is never the product of one person, (mathematically that refers to multiplication) but is always a collaboration. Many people contributed in large and small ways to the completion of this book. First and foremost I want to give thanks to my ancestors for giving me an understanding of mathematics that allows me to share the knowledge I have with others in a way that gives them understanding, and for breathing life into this book allowing me to be the vessel through which this book arrives.

I will be forever grateful to my parents, now with the ancestors (Eunice and Solomon) for being there with me and spiritually overseeing the production of this project and for instilling in me a deep sense of spirituality.

Special thanks to Rev. Phillippe SHOCK Matthews for encouraging my writing, for believing in me and for the professional advice throughout this project.

I would like to pay tribute to two scholars whose influence on others should not be forgotten. The Renaissance Educator and Anthropologist Dr Winters, massive love and respect to you for the tireless effort and fearless approach to the research that you put out there for people like myself to access. You are an inspiration to many including myself so I thank you sincerely.. To brother Billy Bman Byrd, author of 'The Black Room'. Your unwavering support, valuable input and communication throughout reminds me of the iconic tune ('Lean On Me') by our dearly departed brother Bill Withers. You never made me feel that my questions were too weighty or weightless, thank you. To my beautiful children - Qumia, Mylez and Onyeike - who continually remind me that everything I do is for them. They are the unshakeable ornaments in my life.

My Wife, Maxine. The warmest, wisest, sincerest, honest, and most wonderful person I know who makes our house a home – Thank you for your continued understanding and encouragement during our journey. My Queen has taught me some valuable lessons allowing me to unlock *my* hue-man code. For that I will be eternally grateful. Love you…

Finally, I would like to express sincere appreci-love to you, the reader. I hope the information contained within enlightens and empowers you to the reality of yourself.

AUTHOR'S NOTES

I am pleased to welcome you all. Whether you love coded-mathematics, just wishing you knew more, or simply hated the damn thing. There is a whole carbonated experience within this subject and right from the get-go, I wanted this book to be accessible to all those within the whole spectrum who just want to know. To this end, I have kept things as straightforward as possible, but there have been occasions where I thought it worth investigating more effort to fully understand something. With all that said there are actual pockets of mathematics in here: charts, equations, shapes, axioms and a few calculations that I'll walk you through gently. Here what, if you find any of it bothers you, and you don't'' feel like being bothered, just skip over that section. This book has been a work in progress, just as a good life is a work in progress. When my thoughts first turned into a book I had no idea of a title, but I knew the topic in some way would involve mathematics. I didn't just want to write a guide on how to do mathematics, there are plenty of those books out there, some good, others not so good. I wanted to apply mathematics to something that could help us as a people to move forward in our daily lives. A book that would deal primarily with the modern cult of us failing as hue-mans and, as the title suggests, extrapolation of that sense of self to that of the 'truth' from which moral authority seems to stem. It quickly took on the problem of the self in society, a question that turned on the issues of cognition. And so you see "as a work in progress" it kept progressing.

I was told that it was time to stop reading any more books and stop researching and finish the damn book with the theories I have, otherwise, the book will never be complete. There will always be time to read more and write the follow-up books if need be.

In my case, I couldn't be so sure, so I kept reading, and my resulting book has continually changed as I interpolated new resources, new objections and other people's ideas into my own.

During the research period, I was ready to burn the damn thing when my head froze, nothing seemed to register. A voice spoke to me, 'sort yourself out, állow mathematics to flow'. Which in turn created a book labyrinth…

The universe is a system; by understanding that everything in the world is dependent on and can equate to numbers, which can be broken down through various methods. These numbers can then be used to help us to better understand the world and ourselves as individuals where you can discover insights about your purpose and self by working things out. The idea behind your code is that the cosmos and your life are affected by your 'earth-day'. Many will say that other factors such as names, addresses, etc. will add depth to any findings.

I have to disagree with that view, many of us are currently walking around with names that don't rightly belong to us but were forced onto us via slave masters. Many of our ancestors who were forced to cross the Middle Passage by their capturers cross the Atlantic under the written symbol of a number, brand markings or another term. Those who were captured were forced to forget their families, gods, names, and lineages. The first purchase was generally known as number 1, and so on, until these ships were fully "slaved" and ready to sail.

Now, it doesn't matter if you don't fully understand everything contained within this book, just the experience of walking through this journey with me I hope will begin the unveiling of your *code* Don't you think it would be cool for someone to show you the evidence for ONE supreme or universal STANDARD that governs everything? No arm-twisting. No statements of, "You just have to believe." Wouldn't that be great?

The system we live in does not raise us to gods as individuals, but in conjunction with one another, billions of cells and thousands of discrete yet interconnected subsystems of cultures and languages. Imagine the identification of each growing child with the godhead of life, as a whole that would play havoc on old age ethics, and if the infant god does not grow up soon, we shall morph into species of infant god worshippers, and shall continue to play havoc with everything around us, increasing the quotient-level of suffering around the planet, and perhaps throwing those left back into the mythic past.

H. Alan Tansson, Recovering the womb of humanism 2021

In books like *Esotericism and Symbol*, *The Temple in Man*, *Symbol and the Symbolic*, *The Egyptian Miracle*, and the monumental *The Temple of Man*, René Schwaller de Lubicz argued that Egyptian civilization is much older than orthodox Egyptologists suggest. He also argued that the core of ancient Egyptian culture provided fundamental insight into "the laws of creation."

Schwaller, also states that "Nothing in Egypt is accidental or purely ornamental - every element from the type of building material used, the size of the blocks, the dimensions of the walls, number symbolism, the placement of hieroglyphs and symbols, the orientation of the site - all were consciously chosen to have a predetermined effect. Even apparently mundane scenes of daily life can have profound symbolic importance. For example, scenes of the Pharaoh single-handedly overcoming an enemy army are not merely vainglorious boasting; they represent the forces of light overcoming those of darkness."

In *The Temple of Man*, Schwaller demonstrates how the Egyptians were aware of, and consciously used, advanced mathematical concepts normally attributed to the Greeks. One of these was the Golden Section, a mathematical function that occurs throughout nature, for example in the ratios of a spiral galaxy or the orbits of the planets. When used in architecture, it allows the building to become an embodiment of these same universal principles, which were later used in Greek temples and Gothic cathedrals, and which account for some of their power. These elements work synergistically together to express the particular nature of the cosmic principles built into the temple.

Life should not be confused with existence. Existence is a fact, the raw material. Life is what we do with and throughout our existence. It is the sum total of choice (as expressed via actions.)

Pi Ratio.

RESOURCES

PATREON - The Maths Surgery

INSTAGRAM - themathsurgery_

TikTok - themathsurgery_

FACEBOOK - Pi Ratio

GUMROAD - piratio.gumroad.com

EMAIL - maths.surgery@yahoo.com

TRIANGLE THURSDAY, THE MATHS INTERACTIVE
TALK SHOW

GALAXYAFIWE.NET (The De-brain Washing Station)

The Maths Surgery Learning Programs -
https://mathsurgerylearningcourses.com/

To Access Answers to questions in this book click the link
below

https://bit.ly/HuemanCode

BIBLIOGRAPHY

- *GOD Almighty's Grand Unified Theorem (GAGUT): Gabriel Audu Oyibo*
- *Blacks in Science: Ancient and Modern Ivan Van Sertima*
- *The Success System That Never Fails - W. Clement Stone*
- *Star of Deep Beginnings - Dr Charles Finch*
- *The Egyptian Philosophers: Ancient African Voices - Molefi Kete Asante 2000*
- *A Study of Numbers R.A. Schwaller de Lubicz*
- *Supreme Mathematics African Creation Energy*
- *History of Mathematics" Hadi Nurdiansyah*
- *The Hidden Meaning of Numbers Shirley B Lawrence, MSC.D.*
- *The History oF mathematics in Africa Reuben Chukwuma*
- *Recovering the womb of humanism H. Alan Tansson, 2021*
- *Epigenetic Change Open Access Vol 2; issue 2011:1-22 IIOAB-India*
- *Bagnall, R. & Rathbone, D. (2004), Egypt: from Alexander to the copts: An Archaeological and Historical guide. British Museum press, London*
- *Book of the Dead (translated version) Karl Richard Lepsius*
- *Number system: Aurangjeb Alam*
- *The meaning of life: Tzvee Zahavy*
- *Melanin Dr. Llaila Afrika*
- *Isis Papers Dr Frances Cress Welsing*
- *Nile Valley Contribution to Civilisation Anthony T. Browder*
- *Esoterism & Symbol R.A. Schwaller de Lubicz*

- *Discovering The Inner Self David A. Phillips*
- *Your Soul Contract Decoded Nicolas David Ngan*
- *Mathematics and the search for knowledge, 41. Morris Kline*
- *Morals and dogma, 636, L.H Jenkins 1944*
- *The mysteries of magic, 66*
- *A guide to cosmic numbers Wilson Hazel, 1982*
- *The Knot of Time: Astrology and the female experience. River, Lindsay and Sally Gillespie. 1987*
- *Numbers, Their Meaning and Magic, Samuel Wise, 1985*
- *The Secret Doctrine, Volume 1: Cosmogenesis, and Volume 11:Theosophical University Press, 1977.*
- *J. Van Den Driessche, TOE - Theory of Everything.*
- *G. Hancock, Fingerprints of the gods, Random House, 2001*
- *Rajiv Agarwal, Black is a unique colour*

FIGURES

All photos not credited below are in the public domain.

PI Ratio's Recommended Reading

- Nile Valley Contribution To Civilization: Anthony T. Browder
- Supreme Mathematics: *African Creation Energy*
- My Grandmother's Hand: *Resmaa Menakem, MSW, LICSW*
- The Scramble for Africa: *Thomas Pakenham*
- Digitalnomics Walk Away Wealth: *Dr. Phillipe (Shock) Matthews*
- A Mind For Numbers: *Barbra Oakley, PH.D*
- The Black Room: *Billy Bman Bird*
- The Power of Your Subconscious Mind: *Joseph Murphy*
- The Mis-Education of the Negro: *Carter G Woodson*
- The Dancing Wu Li Masters: *Gary Zukav*
- How White Folks Got So Rich: *Reclamation Project*

DISCLAIMER

The information in this book is opinion based combined with research and does not intend to label any organisation or individuals mentioned as anything other than honourable. I also want to add that I don't think the entire self-help/numerology industry is bad, as it's important that consumers of those industries take accountability for their actions. Self-help has many benefits and has certainly benefited me, but only when I approached it from a place of not using it as a "quick fix" for motivation and happiness.

Mathematics teaches you that there must be a balance in whatever it is you are doing.

My goal is to analyse the study of signs, symbols, and numbers to see how these things affect our path in life, comparing my findings with other views and beliefs out there. Treat this as just another perspective and I highly encourage you to do your research.

ABOUT THE AUTHOR
Pi Rah Hotep "The Mathematical Investigator"

The Mathematical Investigator was born in Dulwich, London. I attended university where I read Computer Science and Mathematics. I have had a life-long interest in the study of mathematics, the pursuit of truth being my personal passion. The study of numbers has allowed me to find out more than I could have expected. I am a lecturer in mathematics with over 25 years of mathematical experience. I also use the gift given to me to motivate and empower others to access their mathematical genius. My enthusiasm as a mathematical investigator is infectious. The mathematical methods and processes I share are both relevant and related.

Printed in Great Britain
by Amazon

21951997R00106